Measuring Up ™

to the
Ohio
Learning
Outcomes

and Success Strategies for the Ohio Proficiency Test

Reading

This book is customized for Ohio and the lessons match
the **Ohio Learning Outcomes**. The Measuring Up™
program includes comprehensive worktexts and Ohio Diagnostic
Practice Tests which are available separately.

Level D

W9-BNR-235

800-822-1080
www.OHStandardsHelp.com

PEOPLES
PUBLISHING GROUP
299 Market Street, Saddle Brook, NJ 07663

Acknowledgements

Pg. 12, *Zabali and the Old Woman*, reprinted by permission of SPIDER magazine, February, 1998, Vol. 5, No. 2, copyright © 1998 by Janet Nnakku Nsibambi; pg. 21, *The Treasure Chest*, by Marvene Hall, reprinted by permission of Cricket Magazine, August, 1999 Vol 26, No. 12, copyright © 1999 by Marvene Hall; pg. 39, *Pa's Wonderful Girl*, by Barbara Esposito, reprinted by permission of SPIDER magazine, June 1999, Vol. 6, No. 6, copyright © 1999 by Barbara Esposito; pg. 45, *The Mountain Lion and the Mouse*, by Teresa Pijoan De Van Etter-Spanish American Folktales, August House copyright © 1990; pg. 51, from *Just Hang in There!*, by Jim Janik, copyright © 1998, Highlights for Children, Inc., Columbus, Ohio; pg. 57, *The Caribou Woman-A Yukon-Kuskokwim Delta Eskimo Tale*, retold by Sylvia A. Falconer, reprinted by permission of SPIDER magazine, December, 1999, Vol. 6, No. 12, copyright ©1999 by Sylvia A. Falconer; pg. 73 *Mrs. Fly*, by Paula Matzek, reprinted by Hopscotch for Girls, October/November 1999, published by Bluffton News Publishing; pg. 78, 84, from *The Kindgom Under the Sea*, A Japanese Folktale Retold By Marilyn Bolchunos, copyright © 1998, Highlights for Children, Inc., Columbus, Ohio; pg. 87, pg. 94, *Poetry*, by Eleanor Farjeon from Eleanor Farjeon Poems for Children, copyright © 1938, 1951 published by Harper and Row Publisher, Inc.; pg. 105, *The Owl and the Pussycat*, by Edward Lear; pg. 111, *One*, by James Berry, from When I Dance, Hamish Hamilton Children's Books, copyright © 1988 by James Berry; pg. 113, *The Lion from Dirty Beasts*, by Ronald Dahl, copyright © 1983 reprinted by permission of Farrar, Straus and Giroux, Inc.; pg. 115, *Sneeze*, by Maxine Kumin from No One Writes a Letter To a Snail, copyright © 1962 by Maxine Kumin; pg. 118, *The Camel's Complaint*, by Charles Edward Carryl; pg. 124, *City, City*, by Marci Ridlon, copyright © 1969 by Marci Ridlon, published by Follett Publishing Co.; pg. 126, *Some People*, by Rachel Field published by Simon & Schuster Books for Young Readers, an Imprint of Simon & Schuster Children's Publishing from Poems by Rachele Field (Macmillan, New York: 1957); pg. 130, *Mother Doesn't Want A Dog*, by Judith Viorst from If I Were in Charge of the World and Other Stories by Judith Viorst, Copyright © 1981 by Judith Viorst (New York: Antheneum, 1981); pg. 134, *The Brook*, by Alfred Tennyson; pg. 139, *There's Always Weather* by Langston Hughes, copyright © 1994 by Estate of Langston Hughes, reprinted by permission of Alfred A. Knopf, Inc.; pg. 142, Michael Joseph Ltd. for *The Ants at the Olympics* from ANIMAL ALPHABET, by Richard Digance, published by Michael Joseph Ltd.; pg. 147, Homework by Russell Hoban, copyright © 1964, 1972 by Russel Hoban; pg. 153, *Autumn Silence* by Katie McAllaster Weaver, reprinted by permission of CRICKET MAGAZINE, September 1999, Vol. 27, No. 1, copyright © 1999 by Katie McAllaster Weaver; pg. 156, *Eat-it-all Elaine*, by Kaye Starbird, copyright © 1963 by Kaye Starbird, published by Paul R. Reynolds, Inc.; pg. 167, from *If You Traveled West in a Covered Wagon*, by Ellen Levine, illustrated by Elroy Freem. Text © 1986 by Ellen Levin, Illustrations copyright © 1992 by Scholastic Inc., reprinted by permission of Scholastic, Inc.; pg. 188, *Tickle Theory*, by Rosalind Reid, December 2000, Vol.27, No. 10 MUSE; pg. 192, *Teddy's Bear*, by Janeen R. Adil, reprinted by permission of SPIDER MAGAZINE, May 1998, No. 5, copyright © 1998 by Janeen R. Adil; pg. 198, 202 from *Audubon Society How Wildflowers Get Their Names*, by Jennifer Ewing, published by Scholastic Reference, an imprint of Scholastic Inc., copyright © 1998 by Chanticleer Press Inc., reprinted by permission of Scholastic; pg. 205, *Flicking Tongues*, by Jack Myers, copyright © 1997, Highlights for Children, Inc., Columbus, Ohio, Photographs courtesy of Professor Kurt Schwenk; pg. 210, *Tongue Feats*, by Suzanne Emler, June 1999, Vol. 6, No. 6, SPIDER Magazine; pg. 215, *Blimping Up*, by Carolee Brockmann, New Moon, September/October 1999, reprinted with permission from Twenty-five Beautiful Girls issue of New Moon, The Magazine For Girls and Their Dreams; Copyright © New Moon Publishing, Duluth, MN; pg. 222, *A Dad Who Has Babies*, by Marilyn Singer, February, 2000, Vol. 3, No. 2, CLICK MAGAZINE; Pg. 226, *What Turkeys Eat for Thanksgiving*, by Leslie Dendy, November 1999, Vol. 6, No.11, SPIDER magazine; Pg. 234, *Grandma Moses: Making the Most of Life* by Pat McCarthy, copyright © 1998, Highlights for Children, Inc., Columbus, Ohio; photographs reprinted by permission, AP Wide World Photos, Archive Photos.

Editorial Development, e2 Publishing Services
Pre-Press & Production Manager, Doreen Smith
Project Manager, Jason Grasso
Designer, Jason Grasso
Copy Editors, Amy Kron, Joshua Gillenson

Proofreader, Lee Laddy
Photo Researcher/Permissions Manager, Kristine Liebman
Illustrators, Armando Baéz, Jason Grasso
Cover Design, Armando Baéz

ISBN 1-56256-500-1

Dear Student,

What an exciting year you have in front of you. It is a year in which you will demonstrate your mastery of the Ohio Learning Outcomes for Reading.

The Ohio Proficiency Test measures your ability to comprehend fiction, poetry, and nonfiction. You show your ability by answering multiple-choice questions and writing responses to questions.

This book is designed to help you master the standards and be successful on the test. It provides:

- **A variety of interesting and informative model reading selections**

  When you read these narrative and informative selections, you will apply your before, during, and after reading strategies that help you to read independently.

- **Skill Builder lessons**

  These lessons provide instruction and practice for the standards. Look for the logo Skill Builder.

- **Apply to the Test**

  At the end of each Skill Builder, you will find Apply to the Test. It gives you practice for the skill in the same format as the test.

- **Independent Practice for the Test**

  This lesson asks you to take a sample test. Your confidence will grow as you become familiar with the test format.

Now it's time to get started. If you put your mind to it, by the time you finish this book, you will have mastered the standards and be ready for the test. We wish you a successful year.

Dear Caregiver,

The Ohio Learning Outcomes provide a definition of what each child should know. In Grade 4, mastery of these standards for reading is measured in March by the Ohio Proficiency Test.

Measuring Up to the Ohio Learning Outcomes is designed to help your child master the standards for reading and do well on the test. It provides instruction and practice in the standards as well as preparation for the test. To help your child be successful, it includes:

- **A variety of interesting and informative model reading selections**

  When students read these narrative and informative selections, they will apply their before, during, and after reading strategies. These strategies help them become independent readers.

- **Skill Builder lessons**

  These lessons provide instruction and practice for the standards. Look for the logo SkillBuilder.

- **Apply to the Test**

  At the end of each SkillBuilder is a feature called Apply to the Test. This feature provides practice for the skill in the same format as the test.

- **Independent Practice for the Test**

  This lesson provides a sample test. Your child's confidence will grow as he or she becomes familiar with the test format.

Reading is an essential skill for success in the real world. This book is not easy, but neither is the reading test. Ohio expects its students to measure up to the standards and to be able to demonstrate their mastery of these standards.

Your involvement is a crucial factor in your child's success. Here are some things you can do to help your child be successful.

- Show that you consider your child's success in school important. Each day, talk with your child about what happened in school. Post your child's successful compositions and tests on the refrigerator. Mark dates for tests on the calendar. Celebrate when your child does well.

- Provide a quiet place and a set time for homework. Help your child think through the assignments. Look them over before they are turned in. Of course, this doesn't mean do them for your child, but it does mean provide help and support.

- Show that you think reading is important. Let your child see you read and enjoy books. If your child doesn't have a library card, get one. Take your child to bookstores. Attend book talks or readings with authors at your local library or book store.

- Read aloud to your child. Find a quiet space to read. Share books you loved as a child. Read stories you hold dear, both fiction and nonfiction. Let your child read to you. Listen to books on tape when you ride in a car.

- Keep magazines and newspapers around the house. Surf the Internet together. Look for articles about topics that interest you. Look for answers to questions.

I look forward to working with you this year to ensure your child's success. If you have any question, please do not hesitate to get in touch with me.

Table of Contents

The lessons are aligned *100%* to the *Ohio Learning Outcomes!*

Table of Contents

Table of Contents

Table of Contents

The lessons are aligned 100% to the Ohio Learning Outcomes!

This workbook is 100% aligned to the Ohio Learning Outcomes and provides complete practice for the Ohio Proficiency Test!

As each lesson is completed, place a check mark to indicate mastery or review needed.

Chapter 1: Reading Fiction

Review Needed
Mastery

Ohio Learning Outcomes — Lessons	1	2	3	4	5	6	7	8	9	10	11	12	13	14	15	16	17	18	19	20	21	22	23	24
Given a fiction/poetry text to read silently, learners will demonstrate an understanding of language and elements of fiction/poetry by responding to items in which they:																								
1 summarize the text		●			●				●									●			●			
2 use graphic aids (for example, a table or graph) or illustrations to locate or interpret information				●					●															
3 demonstrate an understanding of text by retelling the information, in writing, in own words		●							●									●	●		●			
4 identify and interpret vocabulary (words, phrases, or expressions) critical to the meaning of the text.		●	●			●			●	●						●	●							
Given a fiction/poetry text to read silently, learners will demonstrate an understanding of language and elements of fiction/poetry by responding to items in which they:																								
5 analyze the text, examining, for example, actions of characters, problem/solution, plot, or point of view		●							●			●	●	●	●		●	●			●			●
6 infer from the text		●						●	●	●							●							
7 compare and/or contrast elements such as characters, settings, or events		●								●							●							
8 respond to the text		●																						
9 choose materials related to purposes, as evidenced in part by the capacity to:		●																					●	
a. choose or identify library resources to locate specific information																							●	
b. select fiction and nonfiction materials in response to a topic or theme		●																					●	
c. choose appropriate resources and materials to solve problems and make decisions		●																					●	
10 demonstrate an understanding of text by predicting outcomes and actions		●																●			●			
Given a nonfiction text to read silently, learners will demonstrate an understanding of language and elements of nonfiction by responding to items in which they:																								
11 summarize the text																								
12 use graphic aids (for example, a table or graph) or illustrations to locate or interpret information																								
13 demonstrate an understanding of text by retelling the information, in writing, in own words																								
14 identify and interpret vocabulary (words, phrases, or expressions) critical to the meaning of the text																								
Given a nonfiction text to read silently, learners will demonstrate an understanding of language and elements of nonfiction by responding to items in which they:																								
15 discern major ideas and supporting ideas																								
16 analyze the text, examining, for example, comparison and contrast, cause and effect, or fact and opinion																								
17 infer from the text																								
18 respond to the text																								
19 choose materials related to purposes, as evidenced in part by the capacity to:																								
a. choose or identify library resources to locate specific information																								
b. select fiction and nonfiction materials in response to a topic or theme																								
c. choose appropriate resources and materials to solve problems and make decisions																								
20 demonstrate an understanding of text by predicting outcomes and actions.																								

As each lesson is completed, place a check mark to indicate mastery or review needed.

Chapter 2: Reading Poetry

Ohio Learning Outcomes	1	2	3	4	5	6	7	8	9	10	11	12	13	14	15	16	17	18	19	20
Given a fiction/poetry text to read silently, learners will demonstrate an understanding of language and elements of fiction/poetry by responding to items in which they:																				
1 summarize the text		●					●						●					●		
2 use graphic aids (for example, a table or graph) or illustrations to locate or interpret information		●					●							●				●		
3 demonstrate an understanding of text by retelling the information, in writing, in own words		●												●		●		●		
4 identify and interpret vocabulary (words, phrases, or expressions) critical to the meaning of the text.				●		●					●	●	●					●		
Given a fiction/poetry text to read silently, learners will demonstrate an understanding of language and elements of fiction/poetry by responding to items in which they:																				
5 analyze the text, examining, for example, actions of characters, problem/solution, plot, or point of view																				
6 infer from the text		●												●				●		
7 compare and/or contrast elements such as characters, settings, or events		●				●		●					●							
8 respond to the text		●												●				●		
9 choose materials related to purposes, as evidenced in part by the capacity to:		●																	●	
a. choose or identify library resources to locate specific information																			●	
b. select fiction and nonfiction materials in response to a topic or theme																			●	
c. choose appropriate resources and materials to solve problems and make decisions										●			●						●	
10 demonstrate an understanding of text by predicting outcomes and actions		●			●	●	●							●				●		
Given a nonfiction text to read silently, learners will demonstrate an understanding of language and elements of nonfiction by responding to items in which they:																				
11 summarize the text																				
12 use graphic aids (for example, a table or graph) or illustrations to locate or interpret information																				
13 demonstrate an understanding of text by retelling the information, in writing, in own words																				
14 identify and interpret vocabulary (words, phrases, or expressions) critical to the meaning of the text																				
Given a nonfiction text to read silently, learners will demonstrate an understanding of language and elements of nonfiction by responding to items in which they:																				
15 discern major ideas and supporting ideas																				
16 analyze the text, examining, for example, comparison and contrast, cause and effect, or fact and opinion																				
17 infer from the text																				
18 respond to the text																				
19 choose materials related to purposes, as evidenced in part by the capacity to:																				
a. choose or identify library resources to locate specific information																				
b. select fiction and nonfiction materials in response to a topic or theme																				
c. choose appropriate resources and materials to solve problems and make decisions																				
20 demonstrate an understanding of text by predicting outcomes and actions.																				

As each lesson is completed, place a check mark to indicate mastery or review needed.

Chapter 3: Reading Nonfiction

Ohio Learning Outcomes

Review Needed / Mastery / Lessons

Ohio Learning Outcomes	1	2	3	4	5	6	7	8	9	10	11	12	13	14	15	16	17	18	19	20	21	22	23	24	25
Given a fiction/poetry text to read silently, learners will demonstrate an understanding of language and elements of fiction/poetry by responding to items in which they:																									
1 summarize the text																									
2 use graphic aids (for example, a table or graph) or illustrations to locate or interpret information																									
3 demonstrate an understanding of text by retelling the information, in writing, in own words																									
4 identify and interpret vocabulary (words, phrases, or expressions) critical to the meaning of the text.																									
Given a fiction/poetry text to read silently, learners will demonstrate an understanding of language and elements of fiction/poetry by responding to items in which they:																									
5 analyze the text, examining, for example, actions of characters, problem/solution, plot, or point of view																									
6 infer from the text																									
7 compare and/or contrast elements such as characters, settings, or events																									
8 respond to the text																									
9 choose materials related to purposes, as evidenced in part by the capacity to:																									
a. choose or identify library resources to locate specific information																									
b. select fiction and nonfiction materials in response to a topic or theme																									
c. choose appropriate resources and materials to solve problems and make decisions																									
10 demonstrate an understanding of text by predicting outcomes and actions																									
Given a nonfiction text to read silently, learners will demonstrate an understanding of language and elements of nonfiction by responding to items in which they:																									
11 summarize the text	●		●							●	●								●	●			●		
12 use graphic aids (for example, a table or graph) or illustrations to locate or interpret information	●			●	●	●				●															
13 demonstrate an understanding of text by retelling the information, in writing, in own words	●									●	●								●	●			●		
14 identify and interpret vocabulary (words, phrases, or expressions) critical to the meaning of the text	●	●						●	●								●	●							
Given a nonfiction text to read silently, learners will demonstrate an understanding of language and elements of nonfiction by responding to items in which they:																									
15 discern major ideas and supporting ideas	●									●	●		●						●	●		●			
16 analyze the text, examining, for example, comparison and contrast, cause and effect, or fact and opinion														●	●	●			●	●		●			
17 infer from the text										●							●		●	●		●			
18 respond to the text	●									●									●						
19 choose materials related to purposes, as evidenced in part by the capacity to:																									
a. choose or identify library resources to locate specific information																									
b. select fiction and nonfiction materials in response to a topic or theme																									
c. choose appropriate resources and materials to solve problems and make decisions																								●	
20 demonstrate an understanding of text by predicting outcomes and actions.											●								●						

Chapter 1 Reading Fiction

What's Coming Up?

In this chapter, you will learn:
- what fiction is
- strategies and skills for reading fiction
- how to analyze words
- how to summarize a text
- how to use illustration to gain meaning
- how to interpret story vocabulary
- how to make inferences
- how to retell
- how to analyze characters
- how to analyze plot
- how to analyze setting
- how to analyze point of view
- how to build vocabulary
- how to answer multiple-choice questions
- how to write a short response
- how to write an extended response

Does This Sound Familiar?

- You are at a Halloween party. You and your friends try to scare each other by telling ghost stories.

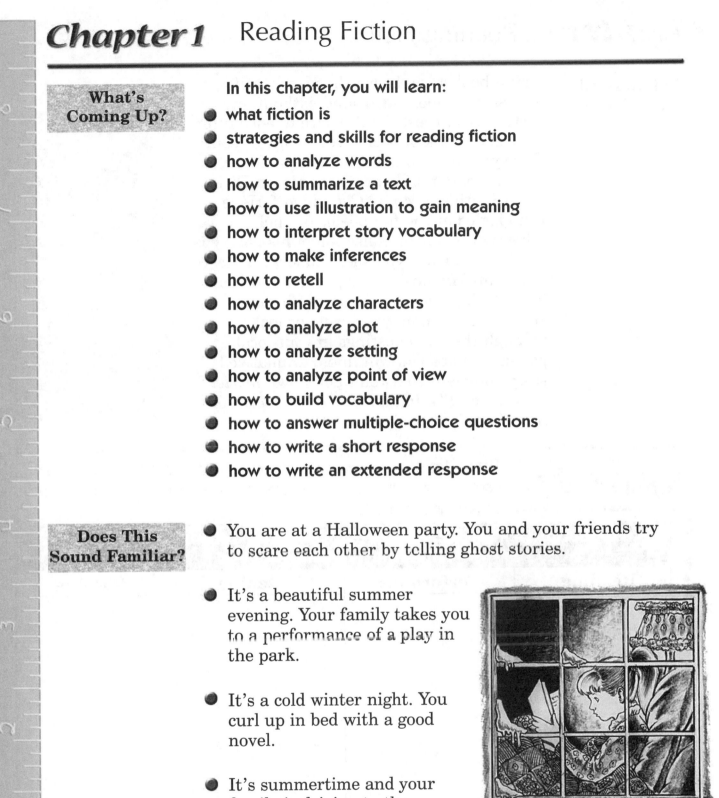

- It's a beautiful summer evening. Your family takes you to a performance of a play in the park.

- It's a cold winter night. You curl up in bed with a good novel.

- It's summertime and your family is driving to the mountains. You listen to an audiocassette of your favorite novel.

Go on to the next page

Chapter 1 Reading Fiction

Visit a bookstore. Learn the pleasure of browsing, or looking around without any particular purpose. You're sure to encounter a novel or book of poems you want to read. Have you met Wolfgang Amadeus Mouse, for example? You'll encounter him in Dick King-Smith's *A Mouse Called Wolf*. Have you giggled at the fun poems of Shel Silverstein? A good collection of his poetry is *Falling Up*. Have you spent time with Mayo Cornelius Higgins? You'll get to know him in *M. C. Higgins, the Great* by Virginia Hamilton. Turn on your radio or look through the movie listings in your local paper. Perhaps you will find a dramatized story you want to listen to or view. *Harriet the Spy*, or *The Indian in the Cupboard*, or *Aladdin* might peak your interest.

 **Warm Up**

Directions Work with a partner. Fill out the chart below. Under each category, list at least five opportunities. Then share your findings with your classmates.

Opportunities for Reading, Performing, Listening, and Viewing Imaginative Literature			
Reading	**Performing**	**Listening**	**Viewing**

What Is Fiction?

Fiction is imaginative literature. It springs from the writer's mind. It is different from nonfiction. Nonfiction tells about true events or provides facts about a subject. Fiction is made-up. It tells you about characters and events that are not real. The people, or characters, in the story, did not really live. The events did not really happen.

Realistic and Fantastic Literature

Some fiction is *realistic*. This means that the characters *seem* like people in real life. The things that happen to them *seem* like things that happen to real people. But the characters never really existed. The events never really happened. They are imaginary. *Sarah, Plain and Tall* by Patricia MacLachlan is a good example of a realistic story.

Some fiction is *fantastic*. This means that the characters may be somewhat strange and unbelievable. The events are not likely to happen in real life. For example, a three-headed talking spider might be a character in a fantastic story. The setting—or time and place—may be fantastic. For example, the story may take place on another planet or in the future. *Peter Pan* is a good example of a fantastic story.

We all like a good story and fiction is fun to read. Fiction also helps us understand life. When we read a good story, we connect with it. We relate the characters and what happens to people we know and things that happen in our own lives.

Go on to the next page

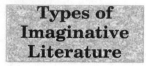 **What is Fiction?**

Types of Imaginative Literature

There are many types of imaginative literature.

Novels A novel is a long work of fiction that tells about made-up people and events. Some novels are divided into chapters, or smaller units. You've probably read many novels already. For example, you may have read *A Million Fish. . . .More or Less* by Patricia C. McKissack.

Short Stories Like its name says, a short story is a short work of literature. Usually it can be read in a brief period of time. You often find short stories in magazines. They also come in collections, such as *The Short Stories of Mark Twain*.

Myths, Legends, and Folktales Myths, legends, and folktales are stories handed down from earlier times. Myths often tell about the gods and goddesses of a group of people. For example, you have probably read and heard myths about Hercules and his dealings with other gods and goddesses of ancient Greece. Legends and folktales often give colorful explanations for natural events. Many contain animal characters. For example, you may have read African tales telling about Anansi the Spider or American Indian legends telling how the rainbow was formed.

Plays A play is a story that is acted out, or performed, usually in a theater or on a stage. Actors take the parts of the characters. You may also see a play on television or you may hear a play on the radio. Sometimes you can read a play in a magazine or book. When you read a play, you see the names of the characters followed by the words they said. You also see stage directions telling the actors where to move and what to do.

Electronic Books Imaginative literature is available on CD-ROM. CD-ROMs allow you to interact with the stories. On some, you can make the characters move. You can find definitions of words you do not know. You can find information about the author.

Special Text Features

Fiction often contains special text features that give it its own unique look.

Chapters

Novels are often divided into chapters. Each chapter has a number and often a title. The titles gives you a good idea of what the chapter is about.

Dialogue

Fiction is filled with dialogue. These are the words that characters speak to one another. Dialogue is set off from the rest of the text by quotation marks.

Illustrations

Many works of fiction are illustrations. Pictures accompany the text and show what the characters and setting look like and what is happening.

Purpose

When you read fiction, set a purpose. Your purpose may be

- simply to get caught up in the excitement of the book and **enjoy** a good story
- to **understand** more about life and people
- to **find out** what life was like at different times or in different places
- to see how characters in stories **solve problems** that are similar to ones you have

Go on to the next page →

Rate

Your rate of reading is how quickly or slowly you read something. Your rate depends on your purpose for reading and the difficulty of the story.

- Read at a **comfortable rate** when
  - ♦ the story doesn't contain difficult words
  - ♦ the story is easy to follow
  - ♦ your purpose is to relax and enjoy yourself
- Read **slowly and carefully** when
  - ♦ the story contains difficult words
  - ♦ the story is a little hard to follow
  - ♦ the story contains many ideas that you need time to think about
  - ♦ your purpose is to study for a test
- **Skim**, or glance through the story without reading every word, when you
  - ♦ are trying to decide whether you want to read it
  - ♦ just want a general idea of what it is about
- **Scan**, or let your eyes glance over the page looking for information, when you
  - ♦ need to find specific information
  - ♦ are trying to find a special episode

Directions Create a personal list of favorites for each category below. Write the title and author. Then write a three-to four-line summary of what the work is about. Be ready to tell your classmates why you chose each work.

My Personal Favorites	
Novel	Title _____ Author _____ Summary _____ _____ _____ _____ _____
Short Story	Title _____ Author _____ Summary _____ _____ _____ _____ _____
Myth, Legend Or Folktale	Title _____ Author _____ Summary _____ _____ _____ _____ _____

Go on to the next page

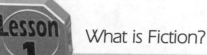

Activity continued

Play	Title _____ Author _____ Summary _____ _____ _____ _____
Poem	Title _____ Author _____ Summary _____ _____ _____ _____
Electronic Book	Title _____ Author _____ Summary _____ _____ _____ _____

How to Read Fiction

How do you get the most meaning from what you read? The strategies and skills below will help you read with greater understanding.

Keys To Success

APPLY READING STRATEGIES

Set a Purpose

Your *purpose* is your reason for reading. Before you read, set a purpose. Then read to carry out this purpose.

Make, Confirm, and Revise Predictions

Make *predictions* or guesses about what you think will happen next. Then read on to see if your predictions are correct. If they are correct, that's fine. If not, revise your prediction and make a new prediction based on the new information.

Retell

Stop every now and then to *retell* the story in your own words. This will help you better understand it.

Summarize

Pause every now and then to *summarize*. A summary contains the most important happenings. It does not contain minor events and details.

Connect Important Ideas

Connect the events in the story. Link the events to characters and places. See how it all adds up.

Go on to the next page

Link Ideas to Your Own Experience and Knowledge

Link what you read to what you already know. Have you ever done something like the characters in the story are doing? Have you ever been to a place similar to the one the author describes?

 Form Pictures

Form *pictures* in your mind as you read. Try to see the people and events with your mind's eye.

Check Your Understanding

Take time to make sure you understand what you are reading. Clear up anything that confuses you. Look up words you don't know in the dictionary. Ask yourself questions and read ahead to find the answers to those questions. Reread parts of the story that are unclear.

Make Inferences

Inferences are intelligent guesses you make after looking at all the details. When you read, you use details from the story to make inferences about characters and events. You use what characters say and what they do to decide what they are like.

LOOK FOR ELEMENTS OF LITERATURE

Plot

When you tell what happens in a story, you are telling its *plot*. The plot is the plan for what happens in the story. Usually the main character faces a problem. The story ends when the problem is solved.

Sequence of events is the order of the events in a story. First one thing happens. Then something else happens. Then a third event happens, and so on. When you read, make sure you understand the order of events.

Writers often tell events in time order. In other words, they tell what happens first, then second, then third, and finally last. Sometimes, though, they mix up the order of events. They start with what happened last to make you curious. Then they tell you the events that led up to this final situation.

Characters

The *characters* are the people in the story. For example, Pippi and Tommy and Annika are all characters in the novel *Pippi Longstocking* by Astrid Lindgren. Sometimes these characters are actually animals. For example, Charlotte is the unforgettable spider in E. B. White's *Charlotte's Web*.

Setting

Setting is where and when a story takes place. The place may be very familiar or very strange. It may be as small as a front porch or as large as the galaxy. The time may be the present, the future, or the past. It may be as small as a summer day or as large as many generations in the life of a family.

Theme

The *theme* is the story's meaning. It is the insight into life revealed through the story. For example, when you read a story about a girl fighting for survival in the wilderness, you might enjoy it because it's a good adventure yarn. You also might come to understand something special about life. Through the girl's experiences, you see that fear is something all people experience, but fear can be conquered. This insight is the story's theme.

READING GUIDE

Directions Put your key strategies to work as you read the following story. The questions on the side will help you.

1
Zabali and the Old Woman
—*Janet Nnakku Nsibambi*

2 Once upon a time, on the plains of East Africa, there lived a mighty king. One day he went out hunting with his son and many servants. But he did not catch any animals, and he was so angry, his servants didn't know what to do.

On the way back to the palace, the King ordered everyone to stop. He was sure he had seen something moving in the brush. He pulled out his spear, but **3** before he could throw it, a baby peacock limped toward him. The poor little thing had lost its mother, and its leg hurt.

4 No longer angry, the King dropped his spear and picked up the little bird. He took it home and had his servants build a fancy house for it. The King loved the peacock so much that only he and his son were allowed to feed it. The peacock's leg healed, and the bird grew big and strong. Its feathers were bright and **5** beautiful.

Now, in the same village, there lived a young boy named Zabali. His family was very poor. They had only **6** one hen, one milk cow, and a small shamba, or garden, where they grew vegetables.

Nearby lived an old woman. Every morning Zabali would carry water for her from the river. Every evening he would bring her firewood. He gave her eggs from his family's hen, milk from the cow, and vegetables from the garden. The Old Woman was so **7** grateful, but she had nothing to give Zabali in return.

GUIDED QUESTIONS

1 Read the title and author's name. Can you **predict** where this story takes place?

2 Check your **prediction**. What is the **setting**? Where does this story take place? Were you right?

3 Try to **picture** the peacock in your mind. How do you think it looked?

4 The king is an important **character** in this story. This is a good place to ask a question about the King. Why did he drop his spear? What do his actions tell you about him?

5 Stop here to **summarize**. What has happened so far in this story?

6 Shamba is an African word. Make sure you are **clear** about what it means. What does it mean?

7 Zabali is the **main character** in this story. **Link** Zabali to your own life. Can you think of people who are kind like Zabali is? Can you think of people who need help like the Old Woman does?

 Measuring Up to the OH Learning Outcomes • Reading

READING GUIDE

Early one morning, Zabali and his family heard loud drumbeats coming from the palace. The King was summoning all the villagers. Zabali's mother and father jumped out of their beds and ran to see what was happening.

The King was very upset. During the night, one of his servants had forgotten to close the door to the **8** peacock's house, and now the peacock was lost.

The King said to the people, "I will give land and many cows to the one who finds my beloved peacock." And with that, he ordered the villagers to start searching.

Zabali's father and mother went home and told Zabali what the King had said. Before they began to search, Zabali said, "I must take some water to my friend, the Old Woman."

The Old Woman was happy to see Zabali. She asked him about the drums. Zabali told her that the King's peacock was missing.

The Old Woman said, "There is a beautiful bird behind my house. It came last night, and I've been feeding it rice. Could it be the King's peacock?"

Zabali went with the Old Woman to look at the bird. Its feathers were so bright and beautiful!

The Old Woman said, "Please take it for being kind to me."

Zabali put the bird in a big basket and ran to the **9** King's palace. The King's guards asked him what he wanted.

"I want to see the King!" said Zabali.

"No one can see the King now. He is too upset. Go away!"

Zabali insisted. "Please let me see the King. Maybe I can make him happy again." The guards just **10** laughed.

GUIDED QUESTIONS

8 Make a **prediction** here. What do you think will happen next? **Read on** to see if you are right.

9 Stop here to **summarize** what has happened in this part of the story.

10 **Question** the guards' behavior. Why do they laugh?

Go on to the next page ➤

READING GUIDE

When the King heard his guards laughing, he was very angry. "How can you laugh when I am so miserable?" he asked.

The guards told him, "There is a small boy here who thinks he can make you happy!"

When the King saw Zabali and his big basket, he was very curious. But Zabali was so excited to be standing near the King that he couldn't even speak. Instead, he opened the basket, and the peacock jumped out. It ran straight to the King.

The King was so pleased that he gave Zabali some of his best land, a big house, and many cows, goats, and chickens. Zabali's family was no longer poor, and they invited the Old Woman to live with them. She was never alone again.

11 That is the end of my story.
12

GUIDED QUESTIONS

11 Did this story turn out as you **predicted** it would? Explain your answer.

12 **Connect** this story to others you have read. Tell about them.

Fluency Tip **F** The name Zabali may be unfamiliar. Practice saying it aloud (za ba le). Say it aloud three or four times until you are comfortable. Then read the story aloud with expression.

What's Expected on the Test?

The Ohio Proficiency Test asks you to read fiction, poetry, and nonfiction selections and answer questions about them. Some of the questions you will answer about the selections are multiple choice. Some require a short written response. Some require an extended, or long, response. In this lesson you will concentrate on answering multiple-choice questions.

Test-Taking Strategies

Read All Questions First

After you read each passage, read through all of the multiple-choice questions that go with it before you start to answer them. This will give you a good picture of what the questions are about. It will also give you time to get your mind warmed up.

Easiest First

Start by answering the easiest multiple-choice questions. These are the questions you are sure you know the answers to. Then go back and answer the more difficult questions.

Keep Track of Time

Don't spend too much time on one item. If you are having difficulty with a question, skip it. Then come back to the question later.

Answer Every Question

Remember to go back to those skipped questions. You will get no credit if you don't answer a question. Start by taking out the choice that seems wrong. Then whittle the choices down until you have only one or two possible answers. If necessary, guess.

Double-check

Double-check your answer. Say the answer to yourself. Does it sound right? Ask yourself if your answer makes sense.

Match Your Answer to the Correct Letter

Fill in the circle by the letter of your choice. A simple mistake is filling in the wrong circle. You know the answer is B but you filled the circle by C by mistake. Don't lose credit because you made a careless error.

Go on to the next page

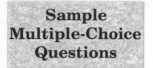

Sample Multiple-Choice Questions

1. This story takes place in
   ○ **A.** South America
   ○ **B.** Africa
   ○ **C.** Hawaii

2. Which item below best describes Zabali's behavior toward the Old Woman?
   ○ **A.** kind and generous
   ○ **B.** mean and rude
   ○ **C.** playful and happy

3. Why do the guards laugh at Zabali?
   ○ **A.** They can't believe a small boy could be clever.
   ○ **B.** They can't believe a small boy could make the King happy.
   ○ **C.** The peacock jumps out from the basket.

4. How do Zabali and his family show their thanks to the Old Woman at the end of the tale?
   ○ **A.** They give her a big house.
   ○ **B.** They return the peacock to her.
   ○ **C.** They invite her to live with them.

5. Which of these items does NOT belong in a summary of this tale?
   ○ **A.** Zabali brings the Old Woman firewood.
   ○ **B.** The King's prized peacock is lost.
   ○ **C.** Zabali returns the peacock to the King.

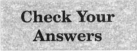

Check Your Answers

How well did you do on these sample multiple-choice questions? Check your answers.

1. This story takes place in
   - ○ **A. INCORRECT** The first sentence of the story tells you that it takes place in East Africa.
   - ● **B. CORRECT** You find out in the first sentence that the story takes place in East Africa.
   - ○ **C. INCORRECT** Hawaii is not in East Africa.

2. Which item below best describes Zabali's behavior toward the Old Woman?
   - ● **A. CORRECT** His actions—he brings her food and firewood—show that he is kind.
   - ○ **B. INCORRECT** His actions show that he is just the opposite of mean and rude.
   - ○ **C. INCORRECT** He may be a playful and happy boy. But these actions do not describe how he acts toward the old woman.

3. Why do the guards laugh at Zabali?
   - ○ **A. INCORRECT** They may believe that a small boy could be clever, but the reason they laugh is that Zabali suggests that he can make the King happy.

   - ● **B. CORRECT** To them, a small boy is too unimportant to be able to make the King happy.
   - ○ **C. INCORRECT** The peacock jumps out from the basket after the guards laugh and the King comes out.

4. How does Zabali and his family show their thanks to the Old Woman at the end of the tale?
   - ○ **A. INCORRECT** The King gives them a big house. They do not give this house to the Old Woman.
   - ○ **B. INCORRECT** Zabali had returned the peacock to the King.
   - ● **C. CORRECT** They do invite her to live with them.

5. Which of these items does NOT belong in a summary of this tale?
   - ● **A. CORRECT** This is an unimportant detail. It does not belong in a summary of the tale.
   - ○ **B. INCORRECT** The fact that the King's prized peacock is lost is an important event and does belong in a summary.
   - ○ **C. INCORRECT** The fact that Zabali returns the peacock to the King is important and does belong in a summary.

The Letters ea

The letters *ea* can spell the long sound of *e* you hear in *be*. Read the following sentence:

> The king loved the *peacock* so much that only he and his son were allowed to feed it.

Notice the word *peacock*. The letters *ea* in this word spell the same long *e* sound you hear in *feed*.

The letters *ea* can also spell the short sound of *e* you hear in *bed*. Read the following sentence:

> Its *feathers* were bright and beautiful.

Notice the word *feathers*. In this word, the letters *ea* spell the short sound of *e*.

A. Directions   Read the following sentences. Tell whether the sound of *e* spelled by *ea* in each italicized word is long or short. Write your answer in the blank.

1. The peacock's leg *healed*, and the bird grew big and strong.

   _____

2. But Zabali was so excited to be standing near the King that he couldn't even *speak*.

   _____

3. *Instead*, he opened the basket and the peacock jumped out.

   _____

4. The King was so *pleased* that he gave Zabali some of his best land, a big house, and many cows, goats, and chickens.

   _____

Activity continued

B. Directions Read the words in the Word Box. Then sort them. Put the words in which *ea* spells the long sound of *e* in the left-hand column. Put the words in which *ea* spells the short sound of *e* in the right-hand column.

Word Box				
plea reach speak leave	seaport breath death leaf	bead breathe thread breach	bread teach dread dead	wealth creak tread feat

long e

short e

_____   _____
_____   _____
_____   _____
_____   _____
_____   _____
_____   _____
_____   _____
_____   _____

Go on to the next page

Activity continued

C. Directions Homophones are words that are spelled alike but are pronounced differently and have different meanings.

1. Write a sentence using the word *lead* when the letters *ea* spell the short sound of *e*.

_____

_____

2. Write a sentence using the word *lead* when the letters *ea* spell the long sound of *e*.

_____

_____

3. Write a sentence using the word *read* when the letters *ea* spell the short sound of *e*.

_____

_____

4. Write a sentence using the word *read* when the letters *ea* spell the long sound of *e*.

_____

_____

Apply to the Test

1. The letters *ea* in the word *peacock* spell the same sound of *e* you hear in

○ **A.** reach

○ **B.** wealth

○ **C.** spread

2. Which word below does NOT have the same sound of *e* you hear in *instead*?

○ **A.** breath

○ **B.** plea

○ **C.** thread

When you summarize, you provide the most important information or events in a brief, or concise, form. You leave out unimportant details or events.

For example, here is a summary of "Zabali and the Old Woman."

> The King finds a hurt peacock, spares its life, and takes it home. The King comes to love the bird, but one night the peacock gets out of its house and is lost. The King offers a reward. A poor boy, Zabali, tells the Old Woman about the peacock. It is behind her house. She gives it to Zabali for his kindness. The King is so pleased when Zabali returns the peacock that he gives him land, a house, and cows, goats, and chickens. Zabali's family, no longer poor, invite the Old Woman to live with them.

Notice that the summary includes only the most important events. It leaves out details like the fact that Zabali's family had only one milk cow, one hen, and a small shamba.

A. Directions Read the story below. Write your responses on the blanks.

The Treasure Chest
—Marvene Hall

My best friend, Robert, and I found the most wonderful treasure chest the other day. It looked like it might have belonged to an old sea captain. The black, dry wood was cracked but hadn't fallen apart yet, and the lid was slightly rounded and fastened with big, solid-gold hinges and latches. All right, maybe they weren't solid gold, but they looked like it.

The trunk was at the county dump, where we'd gone to see if we could find some old rope for the fort we were building in my backyard. Kids shouldn't snoop around the dump, according to Robert's mom, but we liked to explore it now and then anyway. People throw out great things.

Go on to the next page

Activity continued

1. Write a sentence summarizing the information in the paragraphs above.

_____

_____

"I bet there's gold or other neat stuff in here," Robert said when we found the chest. "We'll probably be rich. Are you going to open it, Bill?"

"Give me a minute." I brushed the dirt off the top of the chest and walked all the way around it.

"I'll open it," Robert volunteered enthusiastically.

"I found it first. I'll do it."

I got down on my knees in front of the chest. The latch was stuck, but it opened when I pulled hard on it. The lid creaked back and . . ."

"Nothin'," Robert said. He sounded disappointed.

Activity continued

2. Write a sentence summarizing the information in the paragraphs above.

_____

_____

I was disappointed, too, but I didn't want to let on. "I didn't really expect to find anything in here. But it would still work really great in our fort."

Yeah, let's take it home," Robert said.

"How will we get it there? We can't carry it on our bikes," I pointed out. "It's too big." I thought for a long time. "If we rode home and then walked back, I think we could carry it. Or do you think it's too heavy?"

"We can do it," Robert said. "No sweat."

It took us quite a while to ride home and return, and the dump was closed by the time we got back. But we didn't think anyone would mind if we climbed the fence.

The chest was still sitting where we'd left it. Robert grabbed the handle that stuck out one side, I took the other, and we headed out. It was a bit of a struggle getting it over the gate, but we managed.

3. Write a sentence summarizing the information in the paragraphs above.

_____

_____

Go on to the next page

Activity continued

"What should we use this for when we get it back to our fort?" Robert asked as we walked, the chest between us.

"We can put all kinds of things in it," I answered.

"Like what?"

I thought for a minute. Nothing came to mind. "I don't know right now, but we'll figure something out. Maybe we could put our footballs and baseballs in it. Maybe we could store a rope in it, or maybe food. We can decide later."

Robert nodded but didn't answer. His red hair was plastered to his head, and sweat was running down his face. I was beginning to ache from carrying the chest.

"Let's trade sides for a while," I suggested. "My arm's starting to get tired."

"Mine, too," Robert said.

We stopped and switched sides, then started off again.

"That's better," Robert said. "Not much farther."

I looked down the road. We'd made it down the small hill near the dump but hadn't gotten far. We walked a little more. Then Robert dropped his side with a *thump*.

"Sorry. It slipped out of my hand," Robert said, and he picked up his side again.

We walked on. The chest began to feel heavier than when we started, but though my house was more than a mile from the dump, we were making progress.

"Let's rest a minute," I said.

We plopped down on the trunk and leaned against each other. Sweat poured from both of our faces, and Robert was beginning to turn a little red, like he does when he played baseball too long in the hot sun.

"This thing is heavier than it looks." I hated to admit it.

Activity continued

4. Write a sentence summarizing the information in the paragraphs above.

_____

_____

"I don't think I can carry the dumb thing any farther," Robert grumbled. "Why don't we just leave it here beside the road?"

That was a great idea. Nobody said we had to lug the thing all the way home in one day. It was heavy, and we hadn't thought of a good use for it yet. We could leave it right where it was.

"Maybe we could ask your dad to drive down and bring it back in his van," Robert said. "I bet he'd get it for us."

"No, Dad just left for Uncle George's and won't be back for three or four days. How about your mom getting it for us?"

Robert didn't look at me. "I'm not supposed to go to the dump with you at all. I can't ask Mom to haul something back from a place I'm not even supposed to be at."

I could see want he meant. "Well, let's just leave it here then."

5. Write a sentence summarizing the information in the paragraphs above.

_____

_____

Robert nodded, and we stood up and walked away. We'd only gone a little way when I looked back. I stopped and hung my head. I was sort of disgusted with myself.

"Mom and Dad are always talking about how terrible it is for people to litter up the sides of the roads," I said. "We really shouldn't leave the chest there. It's not right. We put it there, so we should take care of it."

Go on to the next page ➡

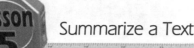

Activity continued

Robert stared at me like he thought I'd gone nuts from the heat. I stared right back at him.

"We can't leave it there," I said, more determined this time.

"Oh, all right." Robert turned and trudged back to the dumb thing.

We traded sides again and carried it for a ways. We put it on the ground and both got behind it and scooted it for a ways. We got in front of it and dragged it for a while. At the top of the hill, we collapsed on the ground, both of us breathing hard.

"I'm too young to die of a heart attack," Robert wheezed. "I think I'm going to go home and tell my mom that I've been to the dump when I shouldn't have and that we have to haul this thing away. Then she'll ground me for a month, and I can rest up."

I laughed at Robert, and suddenly we both felt better.

"Come on," I said. "We're almost there now. The hardest part is behind us."

We made it all the way to my backyard and dropped the chest in front of our fort. Then we sprawled on the lawn, our legs and arms flung out as if we'd died there, and giggled. We'd done it.

6. Write a sentence summarizing the information in the paragraphs above.

_____

_____

Mom came out of the house. "Where have you two been? You're late for supper. What have you been up to?"

I told her. "We went to the dump today and we found this old treasure chest. We're going to put it in the fort. We brought it all the way home by ourselves. Isn't it neat?" I looked at the chest with pride.

Mom turned and looked at it. "You brought that back here again?"

Activity continued

"Again?" What was she talking about?

"That old trunk had been sitting in the attic for years. Your dad just took it to the dump this morning. Why did you haul it all the way back here?"

Robert sat up and glared at me. "You mean this was yours all along? If you thought it would've been good for the fort, why didn't you say something to your dad before he took it away?"

"I didn't know we had this," I answered, feeling sort of silly.

Robert was disgusted. "Good grief," he said and he got up and went home.

How was I to know that treasure chest had belonged to us? I never go up in the attic. It's just full of old junk.

7. Write a sentence summarizing the information in the paragraphs above.

_____

_____

Go on to the next page →

Activity continued

B. Directions   Use the sentences you wrote in Activity A to write a summary of the story.

_____

_____

_____

_____

_____

_____

_____

_____

_____

Apply to the Test

1. All of the following items belong in a summary of "The Treasure Chest" EXCEPT

   ◯ **A.** Dad had just thrown out the old chest.

   ◯ **B.** The two boys find an old chest.

   ◯ **C.** The boys were late for supper.

2. Which statement below belongs in a summary of "The Treasure Chest"?

   ◯ **A.** The two boys are good friends.

   ◯ **B.** The boys think that maybe they can put footballs and baseballs in the chest.

   ◯ **C.** After lugging the chest for a while, the boys decide to leave it by the side of the road.

     Measuring Up to the OH Learning Outcomes • Reading

When you read, look at the illustrations. They can give you a lot of information about what is happening in the story and about the mood, or feeling, the author is trying to create.

A. Directions Look at the illustration above for "The Treasure Chest." Then answer the questions.

1. How old do you think the boys in this story are?

   _____

2. What details in the illustration show you that the boys are working very hard to haul that chest?

   _____

   _____

Go on to the next page

Activity continued

3. Based on the illustration, do you think this story takes place in a big city or a suburban community? What details support your answer?

_____

_____

4. What time of year does it seem to be? What details support your answer?

_____

_____

5. What details tell you that the mood, or feeling, of this story is humorous?

_____

_____

Activity continued

B. Directions Illustrate the ending of "The Treasure Chest." Make sure a reader would be able to "read" your illustration as well as the words of the story. Create your illustration in the frame below.

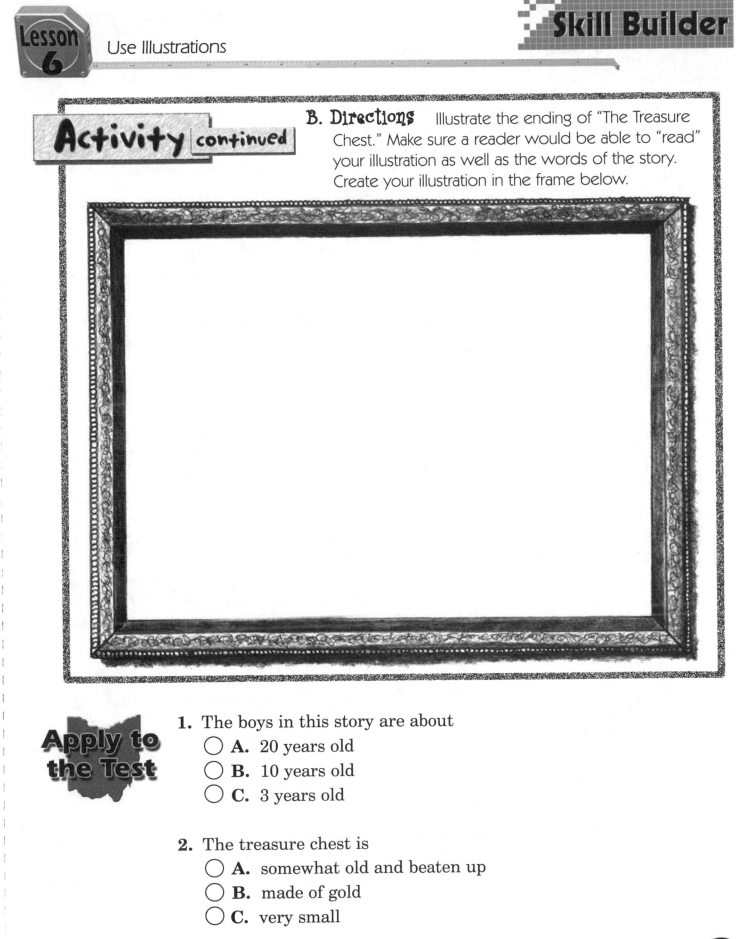

Apply to the Test

1. The boys in this story are about
   ○ **A.** 20 years old
   ○ **B.** 10 years old
   ○ **C.** 3 years old

2. The treasure chest is
   ○ **A.** somewhat old and beaten up
   ○ **B.** made of gold
   ○ **C.** very small

Sometimes a story contains words you may not know. Sometimes you can figure out the meaning of the unknown word from the context. However, other times the context does not help. Then you can find the meaning of an unknown word by looking it up in a dictionary.

For example, look at the following sentence:

> "I'll open it," Robert volunteered *enthusiastically*.

You may not know the meaning of the word *enthusiastically*. The sentence the word is in doesn't give you enough clues to figure it out. Look it up in a dictionary. You will find that enthusiastically means "in a way that shows eagerness and excitement."

Here are some tips for looking up words in a dictionary.

- Words are listed alphabetically. Start with the entries that begin with the first letter, then add the second letter, then the third, until you find the word. Use the guide words at the top of the dictionary page to help you.

- When you need to find a noun, look it up in its singular form. For example, if the unknown word is *attacks*, look up *attack*. Then make the definition plural.

- When you need to find a verb, look it up in its present-tense form. For example, if the unknown word is *sprawled*, look up *sprawl*. Then make the definition of the word fit the past tense.

 **A. Directions** Read each sentence below from "The Treasure Chest." Look up the meaning of the italicized word. Write the definition on the lines provided.

1. His red hair was *plastered* to his head, and sweat was running down his face.

_____

_____

Activity continued

2. "I don't think I can carry the dumb thing any farther," Robert *grumbled*.

_____

_____

3. "I can't ask Mom to *haul* something back from a place I'm not even supposed to be at."

_____

_____

4. "We can't leave it there," I said, more *determined* this time.

_____

_____

5. Robert turned and *trudged* back to the dumb thing.

_____

_____

6. "I'm too young to die of a heart attack," Robert *wheezed*.

_____

_____

7. At the top of the hill, we *collapsed* on the ground, breathing hard.

_____

_____

Go on to the next page

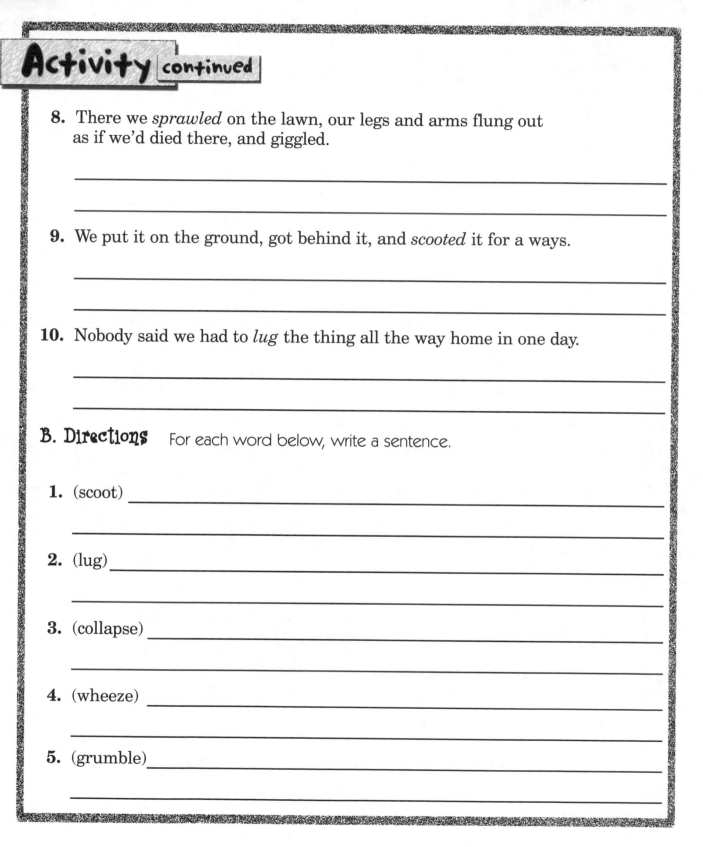

Activity continued

8. There we *sprawled* on the lawn, our legs and arms flung out as if we'd died there, and giggled.

_____

_____

9. We put it on the ground, got behind it, and *scooted* it for a ways.

_____

_____

10. Nobody said we had to *lug* the thing all the way home in one day.

_____

_____

B. Directions   For each word below, write a sentence.

1. (scoot) _____

_____

2. (lug) _____

_____

3. (collapse) _____

_____

4. (wheeze) _____

_____

5. (grumble) _____

_____

Apply to the Test

1. After carrying the trunk such a long distance, the boys *sprawled* on the lawn. *Sprawled* must mean

    ○ **A.** fell

    ○ **B.** spread out and relaxed

    ○ **C.** lugged

2. Mom wondered why the boys *hauled* the trunk back from the dump. *Hauled* must mean

    ○ **A.** dragged

    ○ **B.** lifted

    ○ **C.** slid

Sometimes an author tells you exactly about people and events.

> Emilio was brave and courageous.

Sometimes the author shows you.

> The battle blazed on. The guns blared. The cannons roared. Fear made his knees tremble. But still the soldier pushed on past enemy lines to save his friend.

In the passage above, the author never *tells* you that the soldier is brave. Look at the details—the guns blaring, the cannons roaring, the soldier pressing on to save his friend in spite of his fear. These details help you make the inference that the soldier is indeed courageous.

An *inference* is an intelligent guess you make based on evidence in the story. When you read a story, ask yourself questions like:

- What is this character really like?
- Why is she acting this way?
- How is he feeling?
- Why did she do that?
- Why did the story turn out as it did?

If the author doesn't tell you directly, as you read, find evidence in the story that helps you answer these questions.

Activity

Directions Read each passage below. Write an inference you would make about the character in each passage.

"I want the bandit brought to me now!" shouted the king. He pounded his hand against the side of the throne. He puffed up his chest. His face turned bright red. "Now! " he demanded. His thunderous voice could be heard in the back of the throne room. "Not tomorrow. Not the next day. If the bandit is not brought to me by sunset, you shall not see another sun rise."

1. What inference do you make about the king?

_____

_____

_____

2. What evidence supports your answer?

_____

_____

Randi's birthday was just three days away. "Oh, what shall I buy?" thought Lorraine, as she looked around the mall with her mother.

"A game?" asked Mom.

"A game would be fun. But she has so many!"

"A stuffed animal?"

"Maybe a real animal would do it," replied Lorraine.

As they stepped off the elevator leading to the pet store, they ran right into Randi.

"Oh, gosh!" said Lorraine. I didn't expect to see you here. And she turned bright red.

Go on to the next page ➡

Activity continued

3. What inference do you make about how Lorraine is feeling?

_____

4. Why is she feeling this way?

_____

_____

5. What evidence backs up your answer?

_____

_____

Apply to the Test

1. The king seems to be

  ○ **A.** very happy

  ○ **B.** a kind man

  ○ **C.** very angry

2. Lorraine turns bright red because

  ○ **A.** she is glad to see her friend

  ○ **B.** she is embarrassed because she is looking for a birthday present for Randi

  ○ **C.** she had told Randi she couldn't go to the mall with her because she was sick

Lesson 9 — Independent Practice for the Test

Directions: Read the short story and answer the questions.

Addie and her family live on a farm in South Dakota. A storm comes up that tests Addie's courage.

Pa's Wonderful Girl
Barbara Esposito

Addie coughed as she stuffed oiled rags between the window sashes.

"Get them in tight," Ma said.

Outside, the wind raked gullies into their South Dakota farmland. Pa gulped down his coffee and shook his head. "Looks like another bad one coming."

"If this drought keeps up, our farm will blow away," Ma said. "Maybe we should just pack up and move on."

Pa gave Ma a long look. "We're not quitters. When things get tough, we stick it through."

Bessie mooed from the barn. "Sounds like she agrees with you, Pa." Addie said.

"I'd better check on my sweet, wonderful girl." Pa pulled his neckerchief up around his face and went out.

Addie sighed. "Sometimes I think Pa loves that cow more than us."

Her mother frowned. "Addie! That's no way to talk. You know Bessie keeps us going. We depend on her for milk and cream."

Yes, Addie thought. Bessie's cream waited in the crock. Addie churned it while William played on the floor. When she finished, she put the butter on a plate, covered it, and set it on a shelf in the root cellar. By then, choking dust covered everything in the house. It rippled along the kitchen floor and swirled against the cellar door. The wind had picked up, too, turning the clouds into great rolling waves.

Go On

2Enough.

Ma opened the door a crack. "I've never seen anything this bad." She pushed the door shut. "Your pa should be back by now. Something must have happened. He wouldn't stay out in weather as bad as this." She turned to Addie. I'll go look. Stay here and watch William."

Ma wrapped a shawl around her head. "Don't go out for anything. I'll be right back." She walked head down into the wind, struggling with each step. In a wink, Ma disappeared into the dark wall of dust.

Minutes passed. Addie grew uneasy. What had happened to Pa? Where was Ma now?

Addie heard the clink-a-clink of Bessie's cowbell near the window. She must have gotten loose, because Pa never let her come this close to the house.

What if Bessie got lost in the storm or buried in a sand drift? Addie pressed her ear to the door, listening for voices, but the fierce wind was all she heard. Addie remembered Ma's words: "Don't go out for anything." Should she disobey and take a look, or just wait? Pa loved that cow. If anything happened to Bessie, Pa would be more than upset.

Addie opened the door and peeked out, but it was dark as night. She plunked William in his crib, wrapped a towel around his head, and cautiously stepped out into the storm.

Copying is Illegal.
Measuring Up to the OH Learning Outcomes • Reading

Swirling grit pelted Addie's face. "Bessie!" she yelled, "*Bessie!*"

Addie reached out, groping through the sandy air. When her hand touched something rough, she pulled back. Bessie mooed. She touched the cow again, feeling for Bessie's collar. When she found it, she pulled with all her might, but Bessie wouldn't budge. She found Bessie's rump and gave it a slap. Bessie took a step, then another, until Addie managed to push the scrawny cow into the kitchen.

Addie strained to latch the door, but the powerful wind ripped it off its hinges. She screamed. William wailed.

Addie tried to think. Her hands shook as she looked around for a safe place from the wind. Then she remembered the root cellar. Gently stroking Bessie's neck to calm her, Addie managed to coax the cow down the few steps into the dark cellar. Then she went back for William.

"Mama!" he whimpered. "I want Mama!"

"Me, too," said Addie, bolting the door behind her. Addie hugged William to reassure him—and herself, too. She sang songs and played finger games with him while the wind howled on the other side of the door.

After a while, William asked, "Where's Mama?"

Addie's heart beat faster. Surely Ma and Pa should be back by now, but all she heard were thumps and bangs as the wind whipped through the kitchen above her.

Suddenly, everything grew quiet. Addie quickly unlatched the door. It wouldn't open! Sand trickled through the crack at the bottom.

Addie pounded on the door. "Ma! Pa!" she shouted. William wailed. Bessie mooed. But no one came.

Addie sagged against the dirt wall. They were trapped, alone, in the dark. Ma and Pa were gone. Who would ever look for her? Tears spilled down her checks. Then Pa's voice echoed in her head. "When things get tough, we stick it through."

Addie wiped away the tears. What could she do? She could help William. She picked him up, settled him on her lap, and rocked. "Sh, sh," she said. "W-we'll be all right. Ma and Pa will come."

Go On

William was almost asleep when Addie heard someone call, "Addie! Where are you?"

"In here!" she hollered, banging on the door. She heard Pa's shovel scrape onto the sand. In a few minutes, Pa pulled the door back so the children could squeeze through. Ma hugged them tight.

Addie blinked at the sunlight. Everything looked topsy-turvy. Sand filled the kitchen. Cups and plates were everywhere, and one of Pa's big old work socks rested in William's dish.

"Your pa got hit with a tree limb," Ma said. "I dragged him into the barn, but the wind was so fierce, I couldn't get back to the house. I kept praying you children were safe."

Addie shuffled to the doorway. The top of Pa's plow poked through the sand. Part of the barn roof was gone. She turned to her father. "I saved Bessie, Pa. Your sweet, wonderful girl is in the root cellar, probably chewing up all our turnips."

Pa grinned, swept Addie up, and swung her around. Addie's mouth dropped open. She giggled with dizziness. Her Pa, always so serious, had never done anything like this.

"*You're* my sweet, wonderful girl," he said, turning his face, but not before Addie noticed the tears in his eyes.

1. The author never tells you when this story takes place. Based on details from the story, the best inference is that the events occur

   ○ **A.** in the future

   ○ **B.** about 75 to 150 years ago

   ○ **C.** today

2. At the beginning of the story, how does Addie feel about Pa's calling the cow "my sweet, wonderful girl"?

   ○ **A.** She thinks it's a silly name.

   ○ **B.** She feels a little jealous and hurt.

   ○ **C.** It makes her feel happy.

3. Why does Addie decide to go out into the storm?

   ○ **A.** She is worried about Bessie.

   ○ **B.** She wants to look for her mother.

   ○ **C.** The baby is crying.

4. All the following events happen before Addie and William are trapped in the root cellar EXCEPT

   ○ **A.** Pa calls Addie his "sweet, wonderful girl."

   ○ **B.** Addie coaxes Bessie down the stairs.

   ○ **C.** Pa gets hit with a tree limb.

5. Which word below best describes Addie?

   ○ **A.** Quitter

   ○ **B.** Coward

   ○ **C.** Courageous

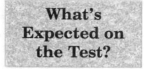

How to Write a Short Response

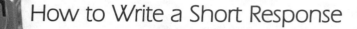

What's Expected on the Test?

On the Ohio Proficiency Test, first you read a selection and answer multiple-choice questions. You learned how to do this in the last set of lessons. Then you will respond to a short-answer question. This is what you will learn to do now.

A short-answer question requires you to think on your own. There are no answers to choose from. However, you can go back to the story as often as you want to find details that help you write your answer.

How long is a short-answer question? Generally, you can answer this type of question in one or two sentences.

Test-Taking Strategies

Read the Question Carefully

Make sure you understand the question. Underline key words in it. Ask yourself: Does my answer fit this question?

Be Complete

Make sure you answer the complete question. Sometimes a question asks you to do more than one thing. Ask yourself Does the question have more than one part? Have I answered each part?

Be Clear

Write what you think as clearly as possible. Ask yourself: Will readers understand what I mean? Is there any way I can make my meaning clearer?

Be Accurate

If you mention the name of a character, make sure you spell the name correctly. If you mention a town, make sure you have the correct name of the town. If you mention a date, make sure you got the date right. Go back to the story as often as you like to check these details.

 Measuring Up to the OH Learning Outcomes • Reading

READING GUIDE

GUIDED QUESTIONS

Directions Put your key strategies to work as you read the following story. The questions on the right will help you. Then read the short-answer question. Think about the story and write your answer.

1 ### The Mountain Lion and the Mouse
—*Teresa Pijoan de Van Etter*

A young brown mountain lion sat by a rain pond. He stretched forward yawning, and then he stretched back, swishing his tail and lifting his rear end high into the air. The warm sun heated the damp earth around him. Thunder and lightning had set the sky to music and lights the night before. Rain had washed away the gray dirt that had collected on every claw, every pad, and every fine, fat, soft layer of fur on his strong body.

2 The mountain lion turned his head just so, just enough, just enough to see his reflection in the rain pond. He glared at his reflection staring back at him. He lifted his upper lip challenging his mirrored image to battle. Then, with a glimmer in his golden eye, he turned and flipped his tail at the poor frightened creature in the rain pond.

The mountain lion lay down under a thick juniper tree. He studied its trunk. This tree was hundreds of years old, and in all those hundreds of years, it still was just an ugly tree. The mountain lion yawned. He licked his powerful front paw, swallowing a fly in the process.

The mountain lion's contentment was interrupted by the sound of something lapping water from the rain pond.

The mountain lion gracefully turned his head. Growling a warning deep in his throat, he called out, "Who is there?"

3 The bobcat respectfully showed himself. "It is I, Bobcat. I have come for a drink of fresh rainwater from the rain pond." The bobcat quickly lay down on the moist dirt and rolled over, showing his stomach.

1 What two **characters** will this tale be about?

2 Make an **Inference**. Why did the mountain lion challenge the image in the rain pond?

3 **Connect** the bobcat's behavior to what you know about animals. Make another **inference**. Why does the bobcat roll over on its back?

Go on to the next page ▷

READING GUIDE

GUIDED QUESTIONS

4 The mountain lion was not amused at his submissiveness[1]. "Bobcat, tell me why is it that I am so strong, graceful, and majestic—and you are but a bobcat?"

The bobcat respectfully answered as he ran, "I don't know, noble Mountain Lion."

The mountain lion frowned. "Humph!' he said.

5 The mountain lion decided he would take a stroll. His strong legs carried him over the little rolling arroyos[2] on top of the mesa. His perceptive ears heard a busy chattering. He turned only so slightly, for he was not one who was easily distracted—or who wished to *appear* to be easily distracted.

There on a sandy pile was a prairie dog. The prairie dog did not see the mountain lion, for he was busy chattering to someone in the other direction. The mountain lion lifted the corners of his mouth and roared, "Prairie Dog, why aren't you as handsome and powerful as I?"

The prairie dog did not wait to answer but dodged into a hole and was out of sight in a blink.

"Too honest to answer, eh?"

The mountain lion went on his way. He stopped at an overlook. The mountain lion could see a grey ribbon far below him with objects moving on it. None of those objects ever came up to his land.

Even the clouds stayed up above him. They moved with the fast wind over the mountain lion's finely shaped head. The mountain lion continued along the
6 side of the escarpment.[3] A lone coyote came trotting up to him.

4 You may not know the **meaning** of the word *submissiveness*. Notice the raised number by this word. It tells you to look at the footnote. What does the word *submissiveness* mean?

5 Use the footnote to find the **meaning** of the word *arroyas*. Using that information as a clue, tell where you think this story takes **place**.

6 What is the **meaning** of the word *escarpment*?

[1]**submissiveness:** giving in without putting up a fight
[2]**arroyos:** dry gullies in the earth, a typical feature in New Mexico
[3]**escarpments:** a steep slope or cliff

READING GUIDE

The coyote was busy sniffing the ground and almost ran into the mighty mountain lion.

The mountain lion let a soft rumble roll out from his throat.

The coyote stopped abruptly and moved to the side. The mountain lion confronted him.

7 "Coyote, why aren't you powerful, muscular, and handsome like me?"

The coyote replied, "You are the most handsome, certainly, Mountain Lion. It is best."

The coyote flattened down and slunk away, hiding behind a chamisa bush.

The mountain lion shook his head, fluffing the fur along his back. His coat was smooth and glistening, and he felt stronger and more powerful today than ever. The mountain lion sat down under a ponderosa pine tree. The tall tree shaded him from the hot sun. The mountain lion yawned. His tail moved slowly up and down. He was bored.

A mouse came scurrying past him. The mountain lion lifted his big paw and placed it smack in front of the mouse.

"MOUSE!!!" the mountain lion roared at the little creature, "Mouse, why am I so strong and powerful, and you so weak and small?"

8 The mouse, without a moment's thought, climbed to the top of the mountain lion's paw. The mouse rubbed his ear with his tiny left paw. The mouse studied the mountain lion for some time, and then he looked down at his paws.

The mountain lion was impatient, "Well, what is your answer?"

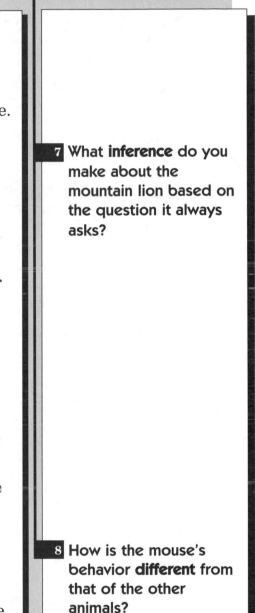

GUIDED QUESTIONS

7 What **inference** do you make about the mountain lion based on the question it always asks?

8 How is the mouse's behavior **different** from that of the other animals?

Go on to the next page ⟩

READING GUIDE

The mouse cocked his head ever so slightly, letting his right ear droop. "I guess this hasn't been one of my better days."

9 The mouse scurried off, eager to be on his way.

Sample Short-Answer Question

10 Describe what the mountain lion is like.

_____

_____

_____

_____

GUIDED QUESTIONS

9 Make an **inference** about the mouse. Why does he scurry away?

10 Notice the key word **describe** in the question. To answer this question, think about people in real life who behave like the mountain lion. Then add up the details and tell what he is like.

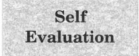 **Directions** Write your answer to the short-answer question on the lines provided above.

Self Evaluation

Ask yourself
- Is my answer complete?
- Does my answer show that I understood the story?
- Is my answer clear and easy to read?
- Are the details I included correct?

   Measuring Up to the OH Learning Outcomes • Reading

How Your Response Will Be Evaluated

Teachers will use a rubric to evaluate your response. This rubric provides the criteria for scoring an answer. The word criteria means "standards against which something is measured." In other words, the rubric tells teachers what to look for in a response.

Your answer will be scored on a scale of 0-2. Getting a 2 means you did the absolute best job possible.

Short-Answer Rubric

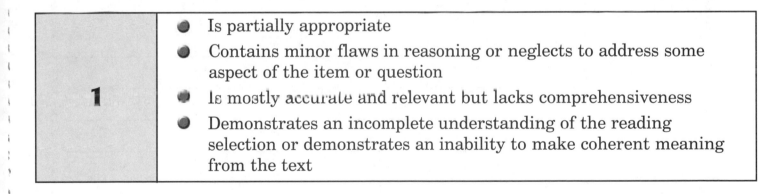

2	• Is complete and appropriate • Demonstrates a thorough understanding of the reading selection • Indicates logical reasoning and conclusions • Is accurate, relevant, comprehensive, and detailed
1	• Is partially appropriate • Contains minor flaws in reasoning or neglects to address some aspect of the item or question • Is mostly accurate and relevant but lacks comprehensiveness • Demonstrates an incomplete understanding of the reading selection or demonstrates an inability to make coherent meaning from the text
0	• Shows no understanding of the item or student fails to respond to item

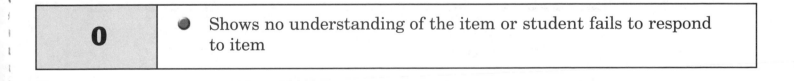

Go on to the next page

How Your Response Will Be Evaluated

Question

Describe what the mountain lion is like.

Sample Answer

The mountain lion is conceited. He thinks he is so strong, graceful, and majestic. He is also a bully. He likes to frighten other animals who are weaker than he is.

Evaluation

This is a 2 response. It shows that the writer understands what the mountain lion is like—conceited and a bully. It includes details that back up the writer's points. It is clear and easy to read.

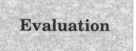 **Directions** Look again at your own answer. Using the rubric, write your evaluation of your answer on the lines below.

_____

_____

_____

_____

_____

Characters are the people in stories. The most important character is called the *main character*. Sometimes the characters seem like people you know. Sometimes they are fantastic creatures like space aliens and hairy goblins. Sometimes they are animals.

Writers give characters personality traits. They may describe how the characters look, how they talk, and even how they feel.

You can learn a lot about characters by listening to what they say. Just like in real life, a character's words tell you a lot about that person. You can also learn about characters by paying attention to what other characters say about them and how they act toward them.

Directions Try to analyze the main character as you read the passage below from "Just Hang in There!" Answer the questions.

from Just Hang in There!
—Jim Janik

The big left-hander on the mound fired the baseball home.

"Hey!" Josh had only a fraction of a second to jerk his head out of the path of the speeding baseball. He flopped onto his back with a thud, the air kicking out from his lungs on impact.

"Strike one!" the umpire yelled.

1. Who is the main character?

_____

2. What has just happened to him?

_____

_____

Go on to the next page

Activity continued

The Mudcat catcher towered over Josh, holding the ball.

"Nice curve, huh?" he chuckled, smirking down at him, then threw the baseball to his pitcher.

"You have to hang in there on that curve ball, Josh!" Coach Schmidt hollered from the third-base coach's box.

3. What do you think the pitcher would say about Josh at this point?

_____

_____

4. What do you think Coach Schmidt would say about him?

_____

_____

Josh, a left-handed hitter, was not used to seeing a left-hander's curve ball breaking away from him. All the right-handed pitchers in the league threw curve balls that curved toward him, right into his swing, right where he liked it.

Josh dusted off his uniform and eased back into the batter's bat.

"Let's give him another curve. That kid's a big chicken!" the Mudcat catcher yelled to the grinning pitcher.

"Just hang in there," Josh told himself. The next pitch came whistling in just like the first, heading right at him. Every muscle in Josh's body screamed at him to get out of the way. He remembered how foolish he had felt jumping away from the first pitch before it broke sharply over the plate for a strike. He decided to hang in there.

But this time the pitch didn't break. It was a fastball. The ball crashed into Josh's shoulder, and he bent over, clutching at the pounding pain in his arm.

 **Activity** continued

5. Why does Josh hang in there?

_____

_____

6. What does his hanging in there tell you about him?

_____

_____

7. What happens when he hangs in there?

_____

_____

Josh slowly trotted down to first base, shaking his hand, trying to coax some feeling back into his arm.

When Josh came up to hit the next time, the catcher shouted out to the pitcher, "Let's put one in his ear this time."

Coach Schmidt called Josh over for a conference.

"Remember to hold your ground on that curve ball. Don't let yourself bail out."

"But how can I tell if it's going to curve?" Josh asked.

"You'll learn. Just watch the seams."

"But what if I'm wrong?" Josh thought. He stretched his stiff arm over his head. Sooner or later he would have to learn to hit the curve.

Go on to the next page

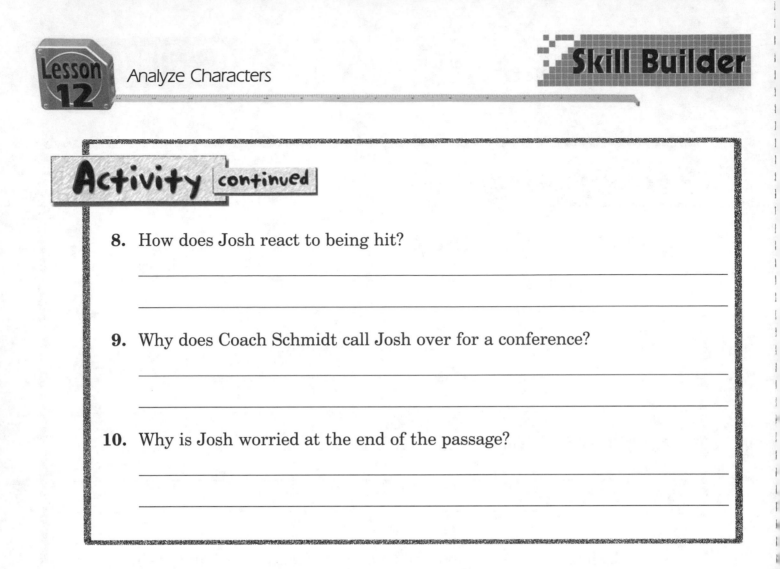

Activity continued

8. How does Josh react to being hit?

_____

_____

9. Why does Coach Schmidt call Josh over for a conference?

_____

_____

10. Why is Josh worried at the end of the passage?

_____

_____

Skill Builder

Apply to the Test

1. All of the following words describe Josh EXCEPT

   ○ **A.** a coward

   ○ **B.** a left-hander

   ○ **C.** nervous

2. Which detail makes you think that Josh is more confident when he plays against right-handed pitchers?

   ○ **A.** He listens to the coach's advice.

   ○ **B.** When a right-hander throws a ball, it curves right into his swing.

   ○ **C.** Left-handed pitchers are better pitchers than right-handed ones.

3. What does Josh's behavior during the game tell you about him?

   _____

   _____

   _____

   _____

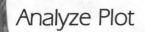
What was the plot of that movie? Did that book have a good plot? Was the plot exciting? How many times have you asked your friends questions like these? They help you decide whether or not you want to see a movie or read a book.

Plot is the plan for what happens in the story. Often the plot starts when the main character has a problem. Then the plot follows the sequence of events that take place as the problem is solved. The story ends with the solution to the problem.

When you read a story, ask yourself these questions:

- What is the problem?
- What happens to solve the problem?
- How is the problem solved?

The events in the plot follow a certain order. *Sequence of events* is the order of events in the story. Another term for sequence of events is time order. When you read, keep track of what happens first, what happens second, what happens next, and so on. Some words help you keep track of the sequence.

First	Next	Later
Second	Following	After
Third	Before	Then
Last	Recently	

In the following paragraph, the words that help you see the sequence of events are printed in italics.

> Kendra and Ricky were helping to build a community garden. *First* they planned a rummage sale to raise money. *Then*, with the money earned through the sale, they bought seeds and bulbs. The beautiful pictures on the packages filled them with dreams of how wonderful their garden would look once they were done. *Next* they planted the seeds and bulbs and watered the soil. *Later* that spring they were filled with delight as the first flowers peeked through the ground. But the most wonderful event happened *after* the flowers were in full bloom. A reporter from the local newspaper interviewed Kendra and Ricky about the garden. They couldn't help but smile *when* a picture of them standing in their garden appeared on the front page of the paper.

A. Directions Read the tale below. Then answer then questions.

The Caribou Woman
A Yukon-Kuskokwim Delta Eskimo Tale
Retold by Sylvia A. Falconer

Long ago, before the white people came to Alaska, there lived an old woman with no husband or children. An Eskimo woman with no husband and no children is a sad woman. She must hunt and fish for herself. She must look for berries and roots alone. In the summer she may be lucky to find enough to feed a squirrel, but in the winter she may go hungry.

The poor woman had traveled from the great Yukon River down to the mouth of the Kuskokwim River looking for food. She went out on the frozen Kuskokwim Bay and cut a hole in the ice with her bone chisel, piling the ice blocks beside her. The wind was blowing across the bay, and she could feel the cold through her fur parka. She propped her sled beside her and covered it with a grass mat to block the wind. Then she dropped a fishing line into the hole. Occasionally she would catch a tomcod.

Go on to the next page

While she was fishing, she looked out at the tundra, which was flat and covered with snow. The sky was gray, and she could see darker clouds coming over the mountains in the distance. Soon it would snow again, and she had barely enough food for her supper. Then she saw a caribou running toward her. To her surprise, it stopped right in front of her, panting, its tongue hanging out. The old woman had never been so close to a live caribou.

Then a strange thing happened. The caribou reached up with its hoof and pulled the skin from its face. Underneath was the face of a woman. "Help me. *Please* help me," said the caribou woman. "Wolves are chasing me, and I am exhausted. I cannot run any farther."

The old woman saw the fear in the caribou woman's face. "You poor thing," she said. She put her fishing pole aside and pushed the ice blocks into a semicircle. "Now you hide right here."

The caribou woman lay near the ice blocks. The old woman sat next to her and pulled the mat around them, hiding the caribou woman.

Soon a large pack of wolves came howling over the tundra. The leader stopped near the old woman and pulled up his face skin. Underneath was the face of a man. "Old lady," said the wolf man, "have you seen a caribou? We have been chasing her all day and we have lost her trail."

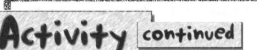

"Yes," said the old woman. "A caribou came running like the wind. She went toward those mountains. I'm sure she's far away by now."

"Not too far for us," said the wolf man. "We shall catch up with her." He pulled his wolf face down and led his pack toward the mountains.

The old woman shivered. "How cold-blooded those wolves are," she said to the caribou woman. "Now you must turn around and run in the direction you just came from. They'll never look for you there."

The caribou woman crawled from under the grass mat. "You saved my life. I can never thank you enough." From inside herself she pulled out a great pile of caribou fat and handed it to the old woman. "May you always find plenty to eat," she said. She pulled her caribou face down and headed off across the tundra.

The old woman cried for joy. She tasted the sweet fat. Now she would have enough to keep her warm all winter.

She dropped her line into the ice hole again and began pulling up cod as fast as she could drop the line. For the rest of her life, she never lacked for fish.

In the summer, she found baskets of greens and berries, enough to share with her neighbors. The Eskimo people say she was rewarded for being kind to the caribou woman. She was never hungry or cold again.

It does pay to be kind to animals.

1. What is the old woman's problem?

_____

_____

Go on to the next page

Activity continued

2. What happens to solve the problem?

_____

_____

3. How is the problem finally solved?

_____

_____

B. Directions   The events below are out of order. Write 1 by the event that happens first. Write 2 by the event that happens next. Continue numbering the events until you reach 8 for the last event. Go back to the story as often as you need to for help.

_____ The old woman tells the caribou woman to run in the direction she just came from.

_____ The caribou lifts the skin from its face to reveal the face of a woman.

_____ The old woman pulls up cod as fast as she can drop the fishing line.

_____ The old woman sends the wolf man toward the mountains to look for the caribou woman.

_____ The caribou woman gives the old woman a great pile of caribou fat.

_____ A large pack of wolves come howling over the tundra.

_____ The old woman sees a caribou running toward her.

_____ The old woman hides the caribou woman under a mat behind a semicircle of ice blocks.

Activity continued

C. Directions Now try it on your own. Read the story starter below. Then write four events in time order.

"The Martians are landing! The Martians are landing!" shouted Wanda.

First_____

_____

_____

Next_____

_____

Then_____

_____

_____

Finally_____

_____

_____

Go on to the next page

1.. Which of the following events happens first?

  ○ **A.** The old woman sees a pack of wolves.

  ○ **B.** The old woman sees a caribou.

  ○ **C.** The old woman finds baskets of greens and berries.

2. At the beginning of the story, what is the old woman's problem?

  ○ **A.** She is tired from traveling.

  ○ **B.** It is too cold to fish.

  ○ **C.** She has to find food for herself and so may go hungry.

3. What happens because of the old woman's kind deed?

_____

_____

_____

The setting is a story is where and when it takes place. Authors include details that help you picture the setting. These details appeal to one or more of the five senses.

Where and when a story takes place may have an effect on the characters. For example, a desert setting in the middle of the summer is going to make the characters feel hot and thirsty. It may also have an affect on the plot. This same setting might lead the characters to take desperate actions as they search for water.

A. Directions   Reread "The Caribou Woman" on page 57. Then answer these questions.

1. Where does the story take place?

   _____

2. Now be even more specific. What is the name of the bay where the woman goes fishing?

   _____

3. At the time of this tale, was Alaska part of the United States? How do you know this?

   _____

   _____

4. What time of year is it at the beginning of the tale?

   _____

5. How does this time of year affect the way the old woman searches for food?

   _____

   _____

Go on to the next page

Activity continued

B. Directions The five senses are listed below. For each sense, list at least two details that help build a vivid picture of the setting of "The Caribou Woman."

The Caribou Woman	
sight	
hearing	
taste	
smell	
touch	

Apply to the Test

1. All of the following details belongs in a description of the setting EXCEPT

   ○ **A.** it takes place today

   ○ **B.** there are caribou and wolves

   ○ **C.** the tundra is flat and covered with snow

2. Which detail below appeals most strongly to your sense of hearing?

   ○ **A.** ice blocks

   ○ **B.** gray sky

   ○ **C.** wolves howling

3. Why is it more difficult for the old woman to find food in the winter than in the summer?

   _____

   _____

   _____

   _____

Point of view is the way the story is told. Sometimes a story is told by a character in it. This character is called the narrator. The character uses the pronoun *I* to talk about himself or herself:

First Person

> I knew if I played it smart I could get my friends to paint the fence for me.

Sometimes a story is told by a narrator who does not appear in the story. This narrator, or storyteller, may focus on one character or on all the characters. The characters are all referred to by the pronoun *he* or *she*.

Third Person

> He knew if he played it smart he could get his friends to paint the fence for him.

A. Directions   Read the following opening passages from stories you have read in this chapter. Tell whether each story is told in the first person or the third person.

1.   Long ago, before the white people came to Alaska, there lived an old woman with no husband or children. An Eskimo woman with no husband and no children is a sad woman. She must hunt and fish for herself. She must look for berries and roots alone. In the summer she may be lucky to find enough to feed a squirrel, but in the winter she may go hungry. ("The Caribou Woman" retold by Sylvia A. Falconer)

_____

2. Once upon a time, on the plains of East Africa, there lived a mighty king. One day he went hunting with his son and many servants. But he did not catch any animals, and he was so angry, his servants didn't know what to do. (from "Zabali and the Old Woman" by Janet Nnakku Nsibambi)

_____

3. My best friend, Robert, and I, found the most wonderful treasure chest the other day. It looked like it might have belonged to an old sea captain. The black, dry wood was cracked but hadn't fallen apart yet, and the lid was slightly rounded and fastened with big, solid-gold hinges and latches. All right, maybe they weren't solid gold, but they looked like it. (from "The Treasure Chest" by Marvene Hall)

_____

4. A young brown mountain lion sat by a rain pond. He stretched forward yawning, and then he stretched back, swishing his tail and lifting his rear end high into the air. The warm sun heated the damp earth around him. Thunder and lightning had set the sky to music and lights the night before. Rain had washed away the gray dirt that had collected on every claw, every pad, and every fine, fat, soft layer of fur on his strong body. (from "The Mountain Lion and the Mouse" by Teresa Pijoan de Van Etter)

_____

Go on to the next page

Activity continued

B. Directions The passage below is written in the third person. Put yourself in the shoes of Herman. Think about what he is thinking and feeling. Rewrite the passage from Herman's point of view, using the pronoun *I*.

Some days it seemed that Herman couldn't do anything right. This morning he rolled over to stop the alarm from ringing. But he reached too far and fell out of bed. After he picked himself up off the floor, he put on his robe and stuffed his feet into his sneakers. But when he tried to walk, he fell flat on his face because his shoe laces were tied together. Finally, he got himself together and went down to breakfast. But when he sat on the chair he tipped it over and fell flat on the floor again.

_____

_____

_____

_____

_____

_____

_____

_____

Apply to the Test

1. In "The Treasure Chest," you learn about events mostly from the point of view of

   ○ **A.** Robert

   ○ **B.** the character identified as *I*

   ○ **C.** Robert's mother

2. How is "The Mountain Lion and the Mouse" narrated?

   ○ **A.** by an outside storyteller

   ○ **B.** by the mountain lion

   ○ **C.** by the mouse

3. At the beginning of "The Treasure Chest," what is the narrator's reaction to the chest?

   _____

   _____

   _____

   _____

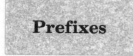

Prefixes

A prefix is a group of letters added to the beginning of a word or word root. The prefix changes the meaning or adds a meaning to the base word. For example, read the following sentence from "The Caribou Woman."

> She put her fishing pole aside and pushed the ice blocks into a *semicircle*.

Look at the word *semicircle*. It is made up of the base word *circle* and the prefix *semi-*.

> semi + circle = semicircle

The prefix semi- means "half." Therefore, the word semicircle means "half circle."

Study the prefixes in the chart below and their meanings.

Prefix	Meaning
semi-	half or partly
hemi-	half
mono-	one
bi-	two
tri-	three

Activity

Directions Use your knowledge of prefixes to answer each question below. Check your answers in a dictionary.

1. If a *bicycle* has two wheels, what is a cycle with three wheels called?

_____

2. Doing something *annually* means that you do it every year. What word means that you do something every half year?

_____

3. If the globe is a *sphere*, what is half the globe called?

_____

4. What is a figure with three *angles* called?

_____

5. If you are *monolingual*, you can speak only one language. What word says that you can speak two languages?

_____

6. *Binoculars* let you see things far away with one or both eyes?

_____

7. Some people wear a *monocle*. This eye glass helps them see out of one or both eyes?

_____

8. Our flag is a *tricolor* flag. How many colors does it have?

_____

Go on to the next page

Activity continued

9. How many people speak in a *monologue*?

_____

10. If you make the *semifinals*, have you won the match yet?

_____

Apply to the Test

1. His sight was bad in one eye only. He decided to wear

  ○ **A.** a monocle

  ○ **B.** binoculars

  ○ **C.** bifocals

2. He flew in an airplane with two sets of wings across Alaska. The plane was called a

  ○ **A.** monoplane

  ○ **B.** triplane

  ○ **C.** biplane

3. In "The Caribou Woman," why did the old woman build a semicircle around the caribou woman?

_____

_____

_____

_____

Directions: Read the short story below and then answer the questions.

> Their regular teacher is out, but the students are surprised when their substitute teacher turns out to be Mrs. Fly.

Mrs. Fly
Paula Matzek

"Yea!" shouted Chick. "No teacher today!"

It was true. At least it seemed to be true. Mr. Digman was nowhere to be seen, and there was no substitute either.

"Yippee!" yelled Amy. "We can have a good time today!"

"Let's have a party!" screamed Chris, dancing wildly around his desk.

Suddenly, at the height of the celebration, a calm, pleasant, high voice was heard above all the commotion. "Good morning, class. Please take your seats."

"What was that?" gasped a stunned Chuck.

"It came from the direction of Mr. Digman's desk," whispered Marie.

"Correct! I am your substitute teacher. Please sit down and get started on your journals."

"There's nothing over there but a *fly*!" exclaimed Chris, who was examining Mr. Digman's desktop.

Go On

Measuring Up to the OH Proficiency Test • Reading   Copying is Illegal.   Reading Fiction **73**

"That's Mrs. Fly to you," said the fly firmly. "Please sit down and get to work."

A shocked silence was followed by a sudden flurry of murmured conversation—"A talking fly!"

"This can't be real!"

"What's going on?"

"Mr. Digman is sick today," explained Mrs. Fly, "but I expect you to follow all of the regular rules and procedures. My nephew Bernie Fly has spent many days visiting your class. Perhaps you remember him observing your reading group."

"Yeah," said Chris," "I remember that fly. He hung around for days."

"Yes," said Mrs. Fly, "that was Bernie, and he always came home just buzzing with excitement. He was quite impressed with the behavior and work habits of your class. So naturally I am thrilled to have this opportunity."

"Let's squash her at recess," whispered Chuck to John.

"Sh-h-h," whispered John.

The class soon discovered that Mrs. Fly could be very strict. Anyone who failed to follow directions immediately found Mrs. Fly sitting directly in his or her ear buzzing angry orders to "pay attention," "sit up straight," "get busy," and "proofread your work."

Marie liked having Mrs. Fly for a reading teacher because Mrs. Fly walked along each line of print as Marie read. Marie never lost her place once.

Mrs. Fly's handwriting lessons were the best. She shuffled around in the chalk dust on the chalk tray and then marched carefully and precisely across the chalkboard, forming every letter perfectly with a series of tiny footprints.

"That's cool!" shouted Chris, forgetting to raise his hand.

"Yes, and you can do it too, just as soon as you learn to walk on walls," chuckled Mrs. Fly.

"I hope she teaches us how to do that during recess," whispered Amy.

But when recess came, Mrs.Fly led the class in a lively game of Simon Says.

"Simon says wave your left wing--oops, I mean arm," giggled Mrs. Fly. Chuck was having so much fun that he forgot all about his plans to squash her.

74   Reading Fiction   Copying is Illegal.   Measuring Up to the OH Proficiency Test • Reading

During science class, Mrs. Fly told her whole life story, including her narrow escape from a hungry spider in the shed behind the gas station last summer.

When the day was over, the students were sad to say good-bye to Mrs. Fly.

"Will you ever be our substitute again?" asked John.

"Yeah, and teach us to walk on walls?" pleaded Amy.

"We'll see," said Mrs. Fly. "In the meantime, you may be seeing my nephew Bernie at school. He's been having some trouble with using guide words in the glossary."

When Mr. Digman returned the next day, he asked the students to write about their day with the substitute.

"Well," he said after reading their papers, "I can't believe that you all got together and collaborated on this wild story. A teacher who can walk on walls and fly around the room? How did you think of such a thing?"

The students just grinned at each other and tried to keep from giggling.

Later, when the reading group was gathered around the table, Mr. Digman heard a faint buzzing sound and saw a small black speck moving around on his open glossary page. "It's that fly again!" he exclaimed.

"BERNIE!" shouted all the students.

1. Who is telling the story?
   - ○ **A.** Chuck
   - ○ **B.** an outside storyteller
   - ○ **C.** Mrs. Fly

2. At first, why do the students think that there is no substitute teacher?
   - ○ **A.** They don't see a person at the teacher's desk.
   - ○ **B.** They expect Mr. Digman to show up soon.
   - ○ **C.** The principal announced that school would close early.

Go On

3. Which detail tells you that this story is fantastic?

   ○ **A.** Mr. Digman is absent for the day.

   ○ **B.** There is a fly in the class.

   ○ **C.** The teacher is a talking fly.

4. Which event happens last?

   ○ **A.** Mrs. Fly tells her life story during the science lesson.

   ○ **B.** Mrs. Fly walks across the chalkboard to form letters.

   ○ **C.** Mrs. fly leads the class in a game of Simon Says.

5. When Mr. Digman returns the next day, he thinks the class must have been collaborating on a story. The word *collaborating* must mean

   ○ **A.** making up

   ○ **B.** working together

   ○ **C.** pretending

6. Why do the children like having Mrs. Fly as a teacher?

_____

_____

_____

_____

What's Expected on the Test?

Another type of question you will answer on the Ohio Proficiency Test is the extended-response question. Just like the short response, this type of question gets you thinking. However, you can go back to the selection as often as you like to help you frame your response.

How long is the extended response? Generally, it's several sentences long. The important thing to remember is that it contains a lot more detail and information than the short response.

The extended response question may ask you to retell. When you retell, you put information or events in your own words.

The extended response question may ask you to write a personal response to literature. When you respond to literature, you interpret what you read and connect it to your life and experience.

The extended response question may ask you to write critically. When you write critically, you judge the merit of something.

Test-Taking Strategies

Stick to the Topic

The more you write, the easier it is to stray from your topic. Stay focused. Make sure everything you write answers the question. Ask yourself: Did I stick to the topic? Did I let my thoughts wander?

Answer All Parts of the Question

An extended-response question may ask you to do more than one thing. For example, it may say, "Tell three ways the turtle outwitted the fox." Make sure you answer all parts of the question. In other words, find all three ways. Ask yourself: Have I answered every part of the question?

Organize

Before you start writing, plan how you will organize your ideas. Look for key words in the question. For example, does it ask you to **compare and contrast** two characters. Does it ask you to **describe** the main character? Ask yourself: Is my organization clear?

Connect Ideas

Use words that connect ideas. These are words like *because, since, after, later, first, next,* and *last.* Ask yourself: Did I use words that help readers move from one idea to the next?

Go on to the next page

READING GUIDE

Directions   Put your reading strategies to work as you read the following story. The questions on the right will guide your reading. Then answer the extended-response question. Think about the story and write your answer.

1 *from* **The Kingdom Under the Sea**

2 **A Japanese Folktale**

3 *Retold by Marilyn Bolchunos*

4   A young boy named Urashima Taro was fishing when he heard children yelling farther down the beach. Moving closer he saw they were teasing a baby sea turtle, turning it over and burying it in the sand.

   "Don't do that," he begged. "If you give it to me, I will give you my fish." Though Urashima was poor and needed the fish he had caught, he was also
5 tender-hearted.

   He carried the little turtle to the ocean. He smiled to see its eager strokes as it swam away.

   Years later, Urashima was fishing on the same beach when a giant sea turtle came out of the water, looked at him with wise black eyes, and said, "I am the turtle you saved years ago. Because of your
6 kindness I invite you to visit the Kingdom Under the Sea."

   "Wonderful," said Urashima. "I would like very much to see it."

   "Climb upon my back," said the turtle. "You will be quite safe."

   To his astonishment, Urashima found he could breathe easily underwater. He watched with interest as the turtle swam past many sea creatures. Finally, at the bottom of the sea, they approached a palace glowing with a mysterious blue light. The walls were
7 made of pearls, shells, and gems. Lovely gardens of waving seaweed surrounded the palace.

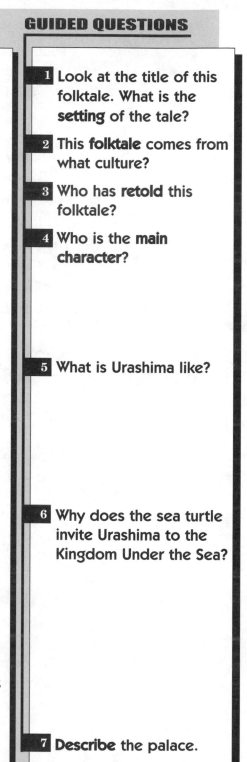

GUIDED QUESTIONS

1 Look at the title of this folktale. What is the **setting** of the tale?

2 This **folktale** comes from what culture?

3 Who has **retold** this folktale?

4 Who is the **main character**?

5 What is Urashima like?

6 Why does the sea turtle invite Urashima to the Kingdom Under the Sea?

7 **Describe** the palace.

READING GUIDE

GUIDED QUESTIONS

Entering a great hall, Urashima saw a beautiful woman. Her long hair wafted about her with the motion of the waves. Her eyes shone like black onyx. She had the kindest face Urashima had ever seen.

"I am the princess Otohime," she said in a voice like water in a gentle brook. "I wish to thank you for helping the turtle. Please enjoy our kingdom at your leisure."

After inviting Urashima to sit down, Otohime shook her folding fan. At once lines of red snappers, flounders, and lobsters began to dance for him. Presently they invited him to dance, and then **8** Otohime danced, too. Urashima was so happy that he felt he could dance forever.

Later he was served many delicious foods. The next day Otohime revealed to him some of the mysteries of the sea—how it controlled the storm clouds, the rains, and the rivers. Urashima wondered if he was in a dream.

Several months passed in this agreeable manner. By this time Otohime and Urashima realized that they **9** were in love. A royal wedding was planned.

10 "Before I marry," Urashima said, "I must visit my home to let my brother know I am all right."

Otohime looked sad. "But you will come back?" she asked.

"Of course," Urashima replied. "I'll be back before you know it."

Then Otohime gave him a small lacquered box. "I am required to give this to you," she said. "It contains something of yours, but you must not open it until you are back with me. If you love me, promise you will not open it."

"I promise," said Urashima. "Do not worry." As the **11** turtle carried him away, Urashima waved until Otohime was lost from sight.

8 At this point in the tale, what do you think will happen to Urashima and Otohime?

9 Check your **prediction**. Did you predict that they would fall in love?

10 Why does Urashima want to return to land? If you were in his place, would you have felt the same way?

11 What do you think will happen in the next part of the tale? Why?

Go on to the next page

READING GUIDE   **GUIDED QUESTIONS**

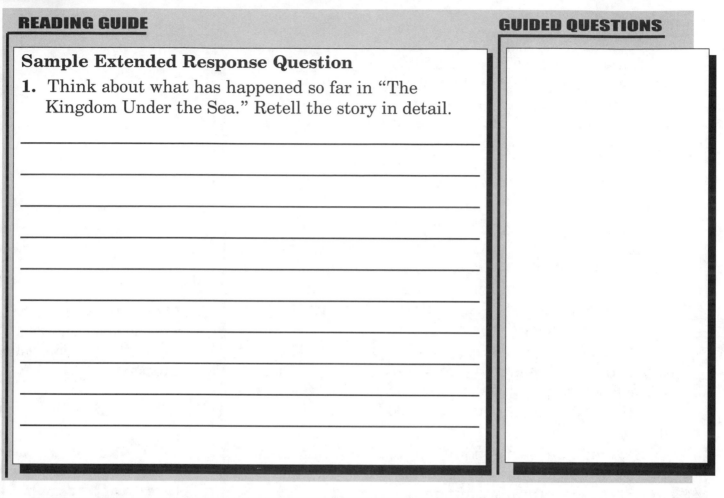

Sample Extended Response Question

1. Think about what has happened so far in "The Kingdom Under the Sea." Retell the story in detail.

_____

_____

_____

_____

_____

_____

_____

_____

_____

_____

_____

 **Directions**   Write your answer to the extended response question on the lines provided under the question.

Self Evaluation

Ask yourself
- Did I stick to the topic?
- Did I answer every part of the question?
- Is my answer well organized?
- Did I connect my ideas?

> Your answer will be evaluated on a scale of 0-4. Become familiar with the rubric below. Teachers will use this rubric to evaluate your answer.

Extended-Response Rubric

4	• Provides extensive evidence of the kind of interpretation called for in the item or question • Is well organized, elaborate, and thorough • Demonstrates a complete understanding of the whole work as well as how the parts blend to form the whole • Is relevant, comprehensive, and detailed, demonstrating a thorough understanding of the reading selection • Addresses thoroughly the important elements of the question • Contains logical reasoning and communicates effectively and clearly (A four-point response may go beyond the requirements of the item.)

3	• Provides evidence that essential interpretation has been made
	• Is thoughtful and reasonably accurate
	• Indicates an understanding of the concept or item
	• Communicates adequately, and generally reaches reasonable conclusions
	• Contains some combination of the following flaws:
	  ◆ Minor flaws in reasoning or interpretation
	  ◆ Failure to address some aspect of the item or omission of some detail

2	• Is mostly accurate and relevant
	• Contains some combination of the following flaws:
	  • Incomplete evidence of interpretation
	  • Unsubstantiated statements made about the text
	  • Incomplete understanding of the concept or item
	  • Lack of comprehensiveness, faulty reasoning, unclear communication

Go on to the next page ➡

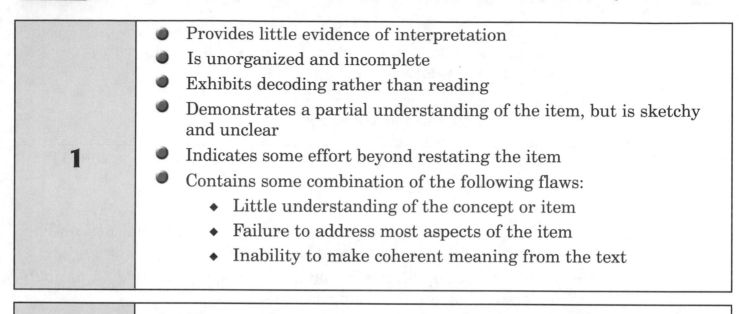

1	• Provides little evidence of interpretation
	• Is unorganized and incomplete
	• Exhibits decoding rather than reading
	• Demonstrates a partial understanding of the item, but is sketchy and unclear
	• Indicates some effort beyond restating the item
	• Contains some combination of the following flaws:
	    ◆ Little understanding of the concept or item
	    ◆ Failure to address most aspects of the item
	    ◆ Inability to make coherent meaning from the text

0	• Shows no understanding of the item or student fails to respond to item

Question

1. Think about what has happened so far in "The Kingdom Under the Sea." Retell the story in detail.

Answer

Urashima Taro sees children teasing a baby sea turtle. He offers them his fish if they will stop, and then he sets the turtle free. Years later when Urashima is grown up, the sea turtle appears again. As a reward for his kindness, the turtle invites Urashima to visit the Kingdom Under the Sea. He travels on the turtle's back to the bottom of the sea. There he finds a beautiful palace surrounded by lovely gardens. He also finds a beautiful woman named Otohime. Urashima and Otohime have a wonderful time dancing with the fish and lobsters. They fall in love. Before they marry, Urashima wants to return home to let his brother know he is still alive. Otohime fears he will not come back, but Urashima promises to return. Otohime gives him a mysterious black box. She makes him promise not to open it until he returns to the Kingdom Under the Sea. As the sea turtle carries him to the surface, Urashima promises not to look inside the box.

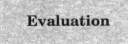 **Evaluation**

This response gets a top score, a 4. It contains all of the key elements of the story, and it provides detail. It is well organized and easy to follow. It shows that the writer completely understood the story.

 **Activity**

Directions Exchange your response with a partner. Using the rubric, evaluate each other's response. Write your evaluation on the lines below.

_____

_____

_____

_____

_____

Retelling is an important skill. It shows that you have really understood what you read.

> When you retell, you put information in your own words. You include in your retelling
> - key parts of the story
> - supporting details
> - major events

You do not include information or details that are not part of the story.

from The Kingdom Under the Sea
a Japanese Folktale
retold by Marilyn Bolchunos

Once back on shore, Urashima thanked the turtle and walked quickly to his village. There had been changes during his absence. Many new huts had been built and many improvements made. "How could they have done so much in so short a time?" he wondered. He saw no one he recognized. This puzzled him because he knew everyone in his village.

When he came to the hut where he and his brother lived, he was shocked to find a large house in its place. A young man stood in the doorway. I am looking for the hut of Urashima Taro," said Urashima. "Can you help me?"

"Urashima Taro?" said the young man. "Haven't you heard? He was lost at sea many years ago. His brother, my grandfather, lives here. Shall I tell my grandfather that someone wishes to see him?"

Overcome with confusion, Urashima shook his head. "No, no," he said. "I must go now."

He returned to the seashore greatly distressed. How could it be that a few months under the sea equaled almost a lifetime on land? Everything was so strange. Had Otohime bewitched him? What had she put in that little box? Urashima felt that he must find out.

He hesitated, remembering his promise, but then with trembling hands he opened the lid. Out came a wisp of smoke, his earth years. As the smoke swirled around him, he became an old man.

Staring into the empty box, Urashima realized that he had lost forever not only Otohime but also his youth. He sank to the sand in shock and despair. For three years and nights Urashima sat grieving, regretting his faithless act.

Finally, one morning as orange dawn broke, he stood up. "What's done is done," he said sadly. "I will go home to my brother, who is also an old man. He will be very surprised to see me. He will want to hear about the Kingdom Under the Sea. Everyone will want to hear about it."

And so they have.

Activity

Directions Retell this part of the story.

_____

_____

_____

_____

_____

_____

_____

_____

_____

_____

Proofreading is reading over your writing to correct any mistakes. Make sure you proofread your extended response before you turn it in.

When you proofread, correct any errors in
- grammar
- spelling
- punctuation
- capitalization

Directions Practice your proofreading skills. Proofread the paragraph below. It contains ten errors.

Back on shore, Urashima is confused. There are sew many changes and the people seem unfamilar. He doesnt know the man living in his brother's house. This strange man tell him that Urashima Taro was lost at sea many years ago. How can that be. Urashima's brother is this mans grandfather. Urashima gets very upset. He thinks that Otohime put a spell on him. Filled with distrust, he wanders what is in the box she gave him? Then he opens the box. It contains all his earth years. Urashima turns into an old man. He has lost both many years of his life and the beautfil Otohime. He can never go back to the kingdom Under the Sea. After feeling sad for a while, he goes to see his brother he tells people about the Kingdom Under the Sea.

Directions: Read the selection and answer the questions.

Maddy says that people think her grandfather is grouchy. Find out why.

My Grouchy Grandpa

by Barry Hoberman

My grandpa Leo lives with us now. Some people say he's a grouch. I guess I can understand why they say that.

He doesn't smile much, especially since Grandma died.

He sure complains a lot: "This coffee is too hot!" "This pillow is too lumpy!" "Channel Eleven comes in lousy on this television!" "Who hid my cigars?"

He's always telling everyone that life was better in the old days.

He tells my parents that they are nuts to live in a big city like Buffalo instead of a small town like Trumansburg, where he and Grandma used to live.

And he can't read a newspaper without groaning and grumbling about "phony baloneys" and "crooks" and "nitwits" and "knuckleheads."

But there's something else about my Grandpa: he really, really, *really* loves me. Do you know how I know?

It's the way he says to me, "Hey, Maddy, the baseball game is on. Come and watch it with me!" And then we watch the game, and he explains everything. He gets all excited when he tells me one more time about his favorite players from the old days, like Robin Roberts and Rich Ashburn and Puddin' Head Jones.

It's the way he always says, "I'll bet Maddy knows the answer!" when anyone asks a question about science or nature or geography.

And it's the way he always wants to buy me an ice-cream cone when we go for a walk–just the two of us–on a summer evening. He knows my favorite flavor is pistachio!

He loves to tell me how Grandma was the prettiest girl in all of New York State when she was young, and how they went to the movies to see *Cinderella* on their first date.

Go On

He always talks about how they loved to go fishing together and take long drives in the country and make their own apple cider every fall.

I don't think my grandpa Leo was always a grouchy guy. My mom says that sometimes people get that way when they get old. I guess that's O.K. Grandpa's never nasty or mean to anyone. He's just kind of grouchy.

He's my grouchy, grumpy, groany, grumbly, growly grandpa.

You won't see a smile on his face very often, but Mom tells me I make him smile on the inside.

Yesterday I asked him, "Grandpa, is Mom right when she says I make you smile on the inside?"

"Maddy," he said, "your mom is a pretty smart lady." Then he gave me the biggest hug ever.

And this time he was smiling on the outside, too!

1. Why do some people say that grandpa is grouchy?

   ○ **A.** He can't read without his glasses.

   ○ **B.** He doesn't smile much.

   ○ **C.** He is old.

2. How does Maddy feel about grandpa?

   ○ **A.** She thinks that grandpa is mean.

   ○ **B.** She likes him only a little bit.

   ○ **C.** She loves him very much.

3. Where does this story take place?

   ○ **A.** Buffalo

   ○ **B.** Trumansburg

   ○ **C.** New York City

4. Which statement belongs in a summary of "My Grouchy Grandpa?"

  ◯ **A.** Maddy makes grandpa smile on the inside.

  ◯ **B.** Grandpa loves to watch baseball games.

  ◯ **C.** Grandpa liked life in the old days better.

5. What is another word used to describe grandpa?

  ◯ **A.** mean

  ◯ **B.** nasty

  ◯ **C.** grumpy

6. What do you think grandpa is really like?

_____

_____

_____

_____

_____

7. Retell the story in your own words.

_____

_____

_____

_____

_____

_____

_____

_____

_____

Choose Materials

1. Browse through your library. Check out all the magazines available. Thumb through at least ten different magazines to identify ones that contain myths, legends, and folktales. Write the names of the ones that do on the lines below.

_____

_____

_____

_____

_____

2. Here are some authors you might like to read.

Betsy Byars	Avi
Crescent Dragonwagon	Isaac Asimov
Patricia McKissick	Allen Say
Yoshiko Uchida	Laura Ingalls Wilder
Robert McCloskey	Kathryn Lasky

Choose two authors from this list. Look through the card catalog in your library. On the lines below, write the titles of books by these authors.

Author 1

_____

_____

_____

_____

_____

Author 2

_____

_____

_____

_____

_____

Home Involvement Activities

Reading Activity

Start keeping a personal reading journal. Select a notebook to write in. Decorate the cover to make it your own. For each book read, fill out the following information:

Title _____

Author _____

Date Read _____

Main Characters _____

_____

_____

What It Was About _____

_____

_____

_____

Would I Recommend It to Someone Else? _____

Why? _____

_____

After you finish reading each book, share your reactions to it with your family.

Listening Activity

Riding in the car with your family or at home in your room, listen to a reading of a story on the radio or on audiotape. As you listen, jot down notes to keep track of the characters' names. Indicate what they are like. Tell what they do. Then talk about what you heard with your family.

_____

_____

_____

_____

_____

Chapter 2 Reading Poetry

Does This Sound Familiar?

- Listening to your favorite song, you sing along with the lyrics—and they're a poem.

- You are reading to a younger sibling at bedtime. You read nursery rhymes—they're poems, too.

- Before a ballgame, you stand and sing the national anthem—another poem.

- Shopping for a birthday card for your best friend, you read lots of cards to find just the right one. You're reading lots of poems.

Poetry Is All Around You!

You've learned much more poetry than you might think. The Mother Goose rhymes you listened to as a toddler were poems. As you grew, you may have read picture books by Dr. Seuss, such as *Green Eggs and Ham*. (When you become an adult, you may still enjoy Dr. Seuss's rhymes.) You may also have read collections of poetry such as Jack Prelutsky's *Something Big Has Been Here* or Shel Silverstein's *Where the Sidewalk Ends*. Some classic books of poetry, such as Robert Louis Stevenson's *A Child's Garden of Verses*, have been enjoyed for more than a century. If you read a magazine such as *Cricket* or *Stone Soup*, you're sure to find poetry in every issue.

Directions The chart below shows four forms of enjoying poetry—reading, performing, listening, and viewing. For each form, list three specific ways. Work with a partner. Share your ideas with your class.

Opportunities for Reading, Performing, Listening, and Viewing Poetry			
Reading	**Performing**	**Listening**	**Viewing**

Poetry
—Eleanor Farjeon

What is Poetry? Who knows?
Not a rose, but the scent of the rose;
Not the sky, but the light in the sky;
Not the fly, but the gleam of the fly;
Not the sea, but the sound of the sea;
Not myself, but what makes me
See, hear, and feel something that prose
Cannot: and what it is, who knows?

Does Eleanor Farjeon's poem define poetry? No. It doesn't define poetry, it *is* poetry. And maybe that's what Farjeon is really saying. Maybe poetry is something that can't be defined, but must be felt. It's something that makes the world beautiful. Sometimes the subject is already beautiful, like a rose or the sea. But even if the subject is not beautiful—like a fly, or a person's mixed feelings—poetry can make it beautiful.

Poetry comes from the writer's feelings, thoughts, and daydreams, just like fiction. The difference between poetry and fiction is not in what it's about. The special thing about poetry is the way it uses language. The poet's job is to find beautiful, new ways of saying things.

In a poem, the sounds and rhythms of the words have to fit the meaning. The word should *sound* the way the poem *feels*.

To make you feel a certain way when you read the poem, the poet might choose certain vowel and consonant sounds. Maybe the poet will use a lot of *s* and *l* and short *i* sounds in one poem, a lot of *k* and *g* and *u* sounds in another. Maybe in one poem, there will be long lines of words that flow in a relaxed way. Maybe in another poem, there will be short, jumpy lines that sound nervous.

Making words sound like feelings is a hard job. When it's done well, it can seize your imagination, energize your feelings, and give you new ideas.

         Measuring Up to the OH Learning Outcomes • Reading

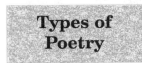

Types of Poetry

There are several types of poetry.

Narrative Poetry A narrative poem is a poem that tells a story. It contains a series of events—a plot. Usually the events are told in the order they happened. (Sometimes, the narrative may look back, or *flashback*, to something that happened earlier.) Dr. Seuss' *The Lorax* is a narrative poem.

Ballad The ballad is a special type of narrative poem. This type began as songs that people sang hundreds, even thousands, of years ago. They sang about murders, sea voyages, kings, robbers, lovers, and other exciting subjects. Because ballads were sung, they had a strong beat, or rhythm. They also had rhymes that were easy to remember. Often, they contained lines or phrases that were repeated over and over. Later, poets began writing ballads on paper. They used a strong beat, memorable rhymes, and repetition to make their written ballads seem songlike.

Lyric Poetry Lyric poetry is poetry that expresses the feelings and thoughts of the speaker rather than telling a story. There may be events in a lyric poem, but narrating them is not the poet's main purpose. Most poetry written nowadays is lyric poetry.

Go on to the next page

Special Text Features of Poetry

You can often tell just by looking at a printed page that it contains poetry. Poetry uses text features all its own.

Lines

A line is the basic building block of poetry. It is usually about the length of one line of type, but it may be longer or shorter. How long the lines should be is one important choice every poet makes about every poem. For instance, the poet may decide that each line of the poem should contain twelve syllables, or that it should contain five accented syllables. Sometimes all the lines in a poem are about the same length. At other times, the poet decides to use different line lengths in the same poem. The length of a line is related to its rhythm. A line is not the same as a sentence. A line of poetry may be exactly one sentence long, but it usually isn't.

Stanzas

A stanza is a group of lines in a poem that forms a unit. Stanzas are to poetry what paragraphs are to prose. (Prose is the opposite of poetry—it's writing that isn't broken into lines. You write prose when you write a composition.) Two stanzas are separated by a line of space.

Rhyme

As you skim a poem you're going to read, you may notice certain groups of letters appearing repeatedly at the ends of lines. This is a clue telling you that the poem may have rhymes in it.

> I took a boat
> to sink or float,
> but on the boat
> there was a goat.
> The goat said, "May I have an oat?"
> I told him, "No, I'm off to vote.
> I'm going to vote for Stacy Stoat."
> The goat said, "Then I'll eat your coat."

If you were skimming that nonsense poem, you'd probably notice the many *oats* right away. Spelling isn't always a clue to rhyme, but it often is. You'll learn more about rhyme in Lesson 2.

Purpose

When you begin reading a poem, it's a good idea to have a purpose in mind, such as

- to **enjoy** the beauty of the poem's language and images
- to **understand** what the poet is expressing about life
- to **find out** about the time and place where the poem is set
- to **solve problems** in your own life by reading about how the speaker of a poem dealt with similar problems

Rate

"Reading rate" means how fast or slow you read. You shouldn't just always read as fast as you can! Choose the right rate for your purpose.

- Read at a **comfortable rate** when
  - the poem's vocabulary is fairly simple
  - the events, ideas, feelings, and images in the poem are not hard to follow
  - you are reading for enjoyment
- Read **slowly and carefully** when
  - the language or imagery of the poem is difficult
  - the poem's ideas, feelings, or events are hard to follow
  - you keep asking yourself, "What does this mean?"
  - you are reading the poem for school
- **Skim**, or glance through the poem without reading every word, when you
  - are trying to decide whether you want to read it more closely
  - want to learn what it is about without reading the whole poem
- **Scan**, or glance through the poem to find specific information, when you
  - are looking for a specific fact, such as the name of a character or the rhyming sounds used
  - are trying to answer a question about a poem you have already read
  - are searching for a specific part of the poem or for the exact wording of something the poet wrote

Go on to the next page

Activity

A. Directions List three poems you have enjoyed—one for each type. You may count songs as poems. If you list a children's book, make sure it really is written in poetry! Write the title and author of each choice. Summarize each choice in three or four lines. Share your list with classmates.

	My Personal Hit List
Narrative Poem	Title_____ Author_____ Summary_____ _____ _____ _____
Ballad	Title_____ Author_____ Summary_____ _____ _____ _____
Lyric Poem	Title_____ Author_____ Summary_____ _____ _____ _____

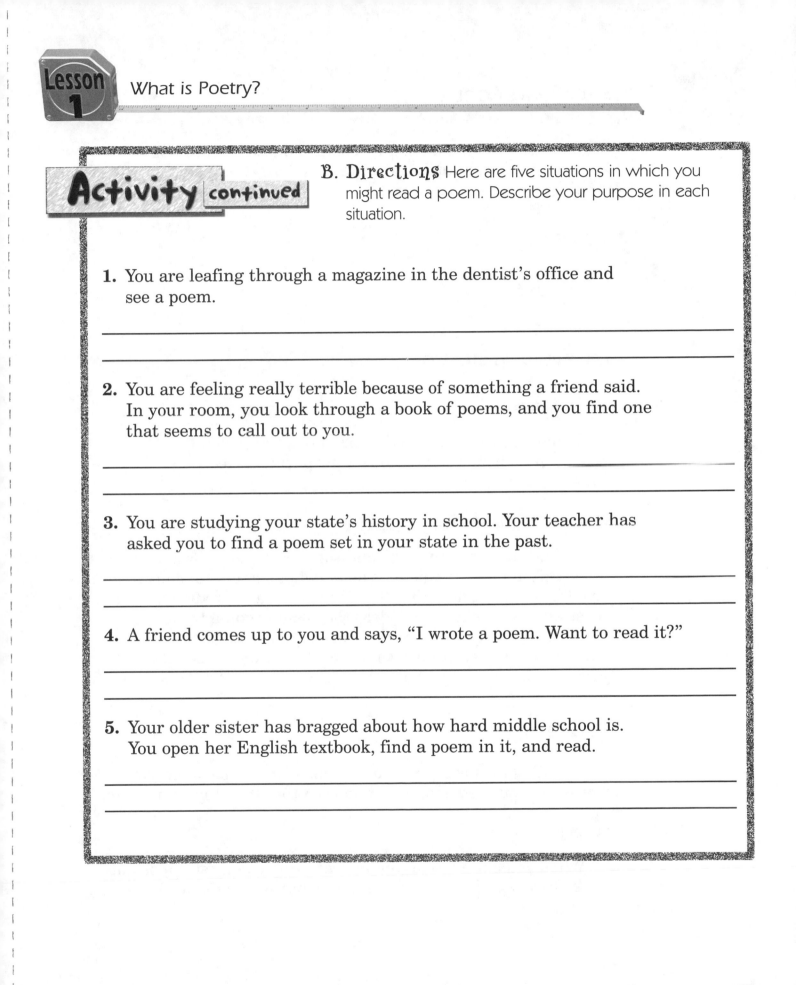

Activity continued

B. Directions Here are five situations in which you might read a poem. Describe your purpose in each situation.

1. You are leafing through a magazine in the dentist's office and see a poem.

_____

_____

2. You are feeling really terrible because of something a friend said. In your room, you look through a book of poems, and you find one that seems to call out to you.

_____

_____

3. You are studying your state's history in school. Your teacher has asked you to find a poem set in your state in the past.

_____

_____

4. A friend comes up to you and says, "I wrote a poem. Want to read it?"

_____

_____

5. Your older sister has bragged about how hard middle school is. You open her English textbook, find a poem in it, and read.

_____

_____

 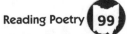

How to Read Poetry

"What does the poem mean?" That's a question you'll be asked many times, in different ways. Here are some strategies and skills to help you answer it.

Keys TO Success

APPLY READING STRATEGIES

Set a Purpose

Whenever you read, you're reading for a reason. Before you read, think about your reason—your purpose. Keep your purpose in mind as you read.

Make, Confirm, and Revise Predictions

As with fiction, you make guesses—predictions—when you read a poem. You make predictions about what's going to happen next. Even if the poem doesn't tell a story, you make predictions about what kinds of feelings and ideas the poem is going to express. Making predictions keeps you reading. You read on to find out whether your predictions were right. If you were wrong, you revise your prediction and make a new prediction about what's going to happen later.

Retell

Retelling means saying what happens in the poem, in your own words. As you read, stop now and then to retell "the poem so far."

Summarize

When you summarize, you are restating the most important facts or events about the poem. Leave out minor details when you summarize.

Connect Important Ideas

A good poem is like a machine in which all the parts are connected to make the whole thing work. Everything counts; nothing is there uselessly. As a reader, try to find the connections.

Link Ideas to Your Own Experience and Knowledge

The key to linking parts of the poem together is to link some of them to things you already know. Perhaps you've had experiences similar to the ones the poet is describing. Perhaps you've felt similar feelings of joy or sorrow.

 Form Pictures

As you read, take a little time to let the descriptions form pictures in your mind. This will help you answer basic questions about what's happening in the poem and whom it's happening to.

 Check Your Understanding

Every now and then, ask yourself how well you understand the poem. Stop to think about things that are confusing you. Reread passages. Look up difficult words. Ask yourself questions about the poem. Read ahead to learn the answers to those questions.

Make Inferences

An inference is an educated guess. You put the details of the poem together with what you already know about life, and you come up with inferences about the poem's meaning.

Predict Outcomes

Usually, the ending of a poem contains thoughts, feelings, or events that are meant to shine a light on what happened earlier in the poem. As you approach the ending of a poem, make a prediction about what it's all going to add up to. What will the poet finally mean? After you've read the ending, think about whether your prediction still fits. If your prediction seems off-target, keep thinking about what the ending means.

Go on to the next page

How to Read Poetry

Compare and Contrast

When you compare things, you find ways in which they are similar. When you contrast things, you find ways in which they are different. A poet may purposely put things into a poem that the reader can compare and contrast, such as two events or two settings. Also, you as a reader can make your own comparisons and contrasts. You can compare and contrast aspects of the poem that seem connected. Or, you can compare and contrast one poem to another, or a poem to real life.

Find Problems and Solutions

Every poem has at least one person in it-the speaker. Chances are, the poem is about some problem that the speaker has faced—a problem about what to do or about how to feel. When you read, ask yourself what problems the people in the poem are facing. Then, look for how they are solving their problems. Keep in mind that the people in a poem don't always solve their problems successfully.

 Measuring Up to the OH Learning Outcomes • Reading

LOOK FOR ELEMENTS OF LITERATURE

Rhythm

When you listen to a song, you can usually hear that the music has a beat, or rhythm. Some notes in the song are stressed more than others. Language has a rhythm, too. When you talk, you stress certain words and certain syllables. When you say, "I'm going out," it might sound like, "*I'm* going out," or like, "I'm going *out*," or like, "I'm *going* out." Rhythm is more important in poetry than in everyday speech. Rhythm in poetry is as important as rhythm in music. The difference is, without musical notes, the rhythm in poetry is usually a little harder to figure out. Reading the poem aloud to yourself can be a big help in this.

Many poems have a regular rhythm—a repeated pattern of stressed and unstressed syllables:

I'm going out
To Smedleyville
And there I'll meet
My brother Will.

If you read those lines aloud, you'll hear that all four have the same rhythm. In reading a poem, if you can get a feel for the rhythm, you're taking a giant step into the world of the poem.

Rhyme

Rhyme is a special way of repeating vowel sounds. When two words rhyme, the last accented vowel sound in each word is the same, and all the sounds after those vowel sounds are the same. *Hear* and *clear* rhyme, because both have *-ear* as their last accented vowel sound. (Actually, it's their only vowel sound.) *Hearing* and *clearing* rhyme. They both have *-ear* as their last accented vowel sound, and the *-ing* sound is also the same in both words. But *earring* and *earphone* don't rhyme. Although the last accented vowel sound is the same in both words, the sounds that follow it are different.

Go on to the next page

 **Figurative Language**

Figurative language is a way of describing one thing by comparing it to another. In figurative language, the words that describe the thing are not literally true. For example, "It's raining cats and dogs" doesn't mean that cats and dogs are falling from the sky. "I'm as hungry as an ox" doesn't mean that the person is really, exactly, as hungry as an ox. It's just a figure of speech.

Two kinds of figurative comparisons are especially important in poetry. They are **simile** and **metaphor**.

A **simile** compares two unlike things by using connecting words such as *like, as, than,* or *resembles.* These little words help point out some surprising, new way of seeing the things that are being compared. For example, "The maple seed spun down slowly to the ground, *like a parachute.*"

In a **metaphor**, two basically unlike things are compared so that they become each other. Linking words such as *like* or *as* are not used. Here's a metaphor: "My son used to be an acorn, and now he's a tall, strong oak." A young man and a tree are compared as if they were one and the same.

READING GUIDE

Directions Use your key strategies to help you follow this poem. The questions will help you.

The Owl and the Pussycat
—*Edward Lear*

1 The Owl and the Pussycat went to sea
    In a beautiful pea-green boat,
They took some honey, and plenty of money,
    Wrapped up in a five-pound note.
The Owl looked up to the stars above,
    And sang to a small guitar,
"O lovely Pussy, O Pussy, my love
    What a beautiful Pussy you are,
        You are,
        You are!
2,3,4 What a beautiful Pussy you are!"
5

Pussy said to the Owl, "You elegant fowl!
    How charmingly sweet you sing!
6 O let us to marry! too long we have tarried:
7   But what shall we do for a ring?"

GUIDED QUESTIONS

1 How is *pea-green boat* **figurative language**? What things are being compared?

2 Which words **rhyme** with which other words in this stanza?

3 Read the stanza to yourself, quietly. Clap your hands at each stressed syllable to notice the **rhythm**.

4 Retell what has happened in the first stanza. Who are the characters and what do they do?

5 Make a prediction: What is going to happen to the owl and the pussycat?

6 Make an inference: What have the owl and the pussycat been up to before they went on the boat?

7 Compare and contrast the owl and the pussycat. In what ways are they alike? In what ways are they different?

Go on to the next page

READING GUIDE

They sailed away, for a year and a day,
    To the land where the Bong-wig grows,
And there in the wood a Piggy-wig stood
    With a ring at the end of his nose,
        His nose,
        His nose,
With a ring at the end of his nose.

"Dear Pig, are you willing to sell for one shilling
    Your ring?" Said the Piggy, "I will."
So they took it away, and were married next day
    By the Turkey who lives on the hill.
They dined on mince, and slices of quince,
    Which they ate with a runcible spoon;
And hand-in-hand, on the edge of the sand,
    They danced by the light of the moon,
        The moon,
        The moon,
They danced by the light of the moon.

Fluency Tip **F**

Practice reading the poem aloud so that you can hear its bouncy rhythms and enjoyable rhymes.

GUIDED QUESTIONS

8 In your mind, **form a picture** of the land where the Bong-Wig grows. What do you see? State some details that go beyond what's in the poem.

9 **Connect ideas**: What does the ring at the end of the pig's nose have to do with the owl and the pussycat?

10 What **problem** is **solved** when the owl and the pussycat meet the pig?

11 **Predict the outcome** of the marriage of the owl and the pussycat. What's going to become of them later?

12 **Check your understanding** of the term *runcible spoon*. How could you find out what it means?

13 Summarize the whole poem briefly. Leave out minor details.

14 **Link your ideas** about the poem **to your knowledge and experience**. Real owls and pussycats don't do the things they do in this poem. Do real people?

Measuring Up to the OH Learning Outcomes • Reading

Lesson 3 How to Answer Multiple-Choice Questions

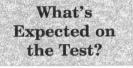
One of the selections you read on the Ohio Proficiency Test might be a poem. You will be asked several kinds of questions about the poem. Some of those questions will probably be multiple choice. Here are some strategies for doing your best when answering multiple-choice questions.

Test-Taking Strategies

First Do the Ones You're Sure Of

Some questions will be easier for you than others. Do those easy ones first. That will give you more time to think about the harder ones. But make sure you answer every question by the time you finish!

Find the Wrong Choices

Even if you don't know the right answer to a question, you may be able to see that one or two of the choices are wrong. Take away those wrong choices. Then you'll only have to choose one right answer out of two or three, not out of four.

Guess If You Have To

You don't get any credit for leaving an answer blank. So make a guess, even if you have no idea. Your chance of being right will be better than zero!

Go through the Questions More Than Once

Suppose you've answered the easy questions, and three hard questions are left. Go through those three in the same way. Answer the easier ones first. Then go back to the hard ones later. Keep going back until you've answered every question.

Avoid Careless Errors

Check your work to make sure you don't give any wrong answers when you really know the right ones. Make sure that you read all the questions and all the answer choices correctly. Make sure you don't miss any tricky little words like *not*. Make sure that if you meant to fill in A, you really filled in A and not B. Make sure you didn't accidentally skip any questions.

Go on to the next page ➤

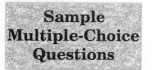

Sample Multiple-Choice Questions

1. "The Owl and the Pussycat" is about two animals who are
   ○ **A.** enemies
   ○ **B.** escaping from hunters
   ○ **C.** in love

2. What do the owl and the pussycat wish they could do?
   ○ **A.** find small birds to eat
   ○ **B.** get married
   ○ **C.** sail forever

3. What other animals appear in the poem?
   ○ **A.** quinces and minces
   ○ **B.** a walrus and an oyster
   ○ **C.** a turkey and a pig

4. What is special about the last four lines of each stanza?
   ○ **A.** They are all the same.
   ○ **B.** They all end in the word *moon*.
   ○ **C.** The two last lines repeat the two next-to-last lines, in reverse order.

5. What is the tone of the poem?
   ○ **A.** serious
   ○ **B.** humorous
   ○ **C.** scary

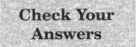
Check Your Answers

Check how well you did on these sample questions. If you got any wrong, think about why.

1. "The Owl and the Pussycat" is about two animals who are

   ○ A. **INCORRECT** The owl and the pussycat sail away together.

   ○ B. **INCORRECT** There are no hunters in the poem.

   ● C. **CORRECT** The owl sings of his love for the pussycat in the first stanza.

2. What do the owl and the pussycat wish they could do?

   ○ A. **INCORRECT** In the poem, the owl and pussycat eat like people. They don't hunt.

   ● B. **CORRECT** The pussycat says, "O let us to marry!" in the third line of the second stanza.

   ○ C. **INCORRECT** They stop at the land where the Bong-wig grows. They never say they wish they could sail longer.

3. What other animals appear in the poem?

   ○ A. **INCORRECT** Quince and mince are foods.

   ○ B. **INCORRECT** There is no walrus or oyster in the poem.

   ● C. **CORRECT** The turkey performs the wedding. The pig lends his ring.

4. What is special about the last four lines of each stanza?

   ○ A. **INCORRECT** Some lines are repeated, but not all.

   ○ B. **INCORRECT** They all end in *moon* in the last stanza, but not in the other two stanzas.

   ● C. **CORRECT** In each stanza, lines 8 and 11 are the same, and lines 9 and 10 are the same.

5. What is the tone of the poem?

   ○ A. **INCORRECT** The poem is full of nonsense words and silly behavior.

   ● B. **CORRECT** The idea of an owl and a pussycat getting married is funny, and the poet's use of words is playful.

   ○ C. **INCORRECT** There's nothing scary about the poem.

Compound Words

A compound word is a larger word that is made up of two or more smaller words. For example:

blue	+	berry	=	blueberry
court	+	house	=	courthouse
suit	+	case	=	suitcase
some	+	one	=	someone

Compound words are often made up to describe new machines or new ideas. Examples are *videotape* and *skateboard*.

How can you tell whether a word is a compound word? Take it apart. If each of its main parts can stand alone as a separate word, it is a compound word.

Downtown	=	down	+	town

Down and *town* are both words, so *downtown* is a compound word.

Downward	=	down	+	ward

Down is a word, but *ward*, meaning "toward," can't stand alone as a word. So *downward* isn't a compound word.

Directions Read the following poem and answer the questions.

One

—James Berry

Only one of me
and nobody can get a second one
from a photocopy machine.

Nobody has the fingerprints I have.
Nobody can cry my tears, or laugh my laugh
or have my expectancy when I wait.

But anybody can mimic my dance with my dog.
Anybody can howl how I sing out of tune.
And mirrors can show me multiplied
many times, say, dressed up in red
or dressed up in gray.

Nobody can get into my clothes for me
or feel my fall for me, or do my running.
Nobody hears my music for me, either.

I am just this one.
Nobody else makes the words
I shape with sound, when I talk.

But anybody can act how I stutter in a rage.
Anybody can copy echoes I make.
And mirrors can show me multiplied
many times, say, dressed up in green
or dressed up in blue.

Go on to the next page

Activity continued

1. What is the first compound word in the poem?_____

2. What compound word in the poem means the opposite of that first compound word?

   _____

3. What compound word in the poem refers to something that is different for every person?

   _____

4. What compound word in the poem refers to a machine invented in the twentieth century?

   _____

5. What small word is part of two different compound words in the poem?

   _____

Apply to the Test

1. Which very short word in the poem "One" is a compound word?

   ○ **A.** only

   ○ **B.** one

   ○ **C.** into

2. Which of the following is a compound word?

   ○ **A.** noon

   ○ **B.** nowhere

   ○ **C.** none

The *outcome* of a poem is what happens at the end. For example, the outcome of "The Owl and the Pussycat" is that the owl and the pussycat get married and celebrate.

An outcome can also be something that happens after the end of the poem. For example, you might guess that after they get married, the owl and the pussycat realize how different they are. That is an outcome that might happen after the poem ends.

As you read a poem, it's fun to predict the outcome. A prediction is basically just a guess, based on what you already know.

Directions Read the following poem and answer the questions.

The Lion
—*Roald Dahl*

The lion just adores to eat
A lot of red and tender meat,
And if you ask the lion what
Is much the tenderest of the lot,
He will not say a roast of lamb
Or curried beef or devilled ham
Or crispy pork or corned beef hash
Or sausages or mutton mash.
Then could it be a big plump hen?
He answers no. What is it, then?
Oh, lion dear, could I not make
You happy with a lovely steak?
Could I entice you from your lair
With rabbit-pie or roasted hare?
The lion smiled and shook his head.
He came up very close and said,
"The meat I am about to chew
Is neither steak nor chops. IT'S YOU."

Go on to the next page

Measuring Up to the OH Learning Outcomes • Reading   Copying is Illegal.   Reading Poetry **113**

Activity continued

1. What outcome did you predict for this poem?

   _____

2. At what point in the poem did you make that prediction?

   _____

3. On what did you base your prediction?

   _____

   _____

4. Did your prediction come true? Explain.

   _____

   _____

5. Predict a different outcome for the poem-one it might have had, but didn't.

   _____

   _____

1. Which phrase expresses the outcome of the poem?

   ○ **A.** A lot of red and tender meat

   ○ **B.** He answers no.

   ○ **C.** IT'S YOU.

2. Which of the following sentences predicts an outcome that might happen after the poem ends?

   ○ **A.** The lion doesn't want sausages or mutton mash.

   ○ **B.** The lion loves red meat.

   ○ **C.** The speaker escapes from the lion.

Directions: Read the selection and answer the questions.

Sneeze

Maxine Kumin

There's a
sort of a
tickle
the size of a
nickel,
a bit like the
prickle
of sweet-sour
pickle;

it's a
quivery
shiver
the shape of a
sliver,
like eels in a
river;

a kind of a
wiggle
that starts as a
jiggle
and joggles
its way to a
tease,

which I
cannot
suppress
any longer,
I guess, so pardon me,
please, while I
sneeze.

Go On

1. What is this poem about?

   ○ **A.** Sneezing and not being able to find a handkerchief or tissue.

   ○ **B.** Disturbing a classroom with loud sneezes.

   ○ **C.** Feeling a sneeze coming on, and trying not to sneeze, but having to sneeze anyway.

2. What feeling does the speaker compare to "a/ quivery/ shiver/ the shape of a /sliver,/ like eels in a/ river?"

   ○ **A.** The feeling that everyone is watching you.

   ○ **B.** The feeling of having to sneeze.

   ○ **C.** The feeling of having a sore throat.

3. In the lines, "which I/ cannot/ suppress/ any longer,/ I guess," what can't the speaker do?

   ○ **A.** come to school when she's sick

   ○ **B.** hold back her sneeze

   ○ **C.** play with her friends

4. What is special about the words *tickle*, *nickel*, *prickle*, and *pickle* in the first stanza?

   ○ **A.** They all describe funny feelings.

   ○ **B.** They all end in *le*.

   ○ **C.** They all rhyme.

5. What would you notice about the poem just by looking at it, without reading its words?

   ○ **A.** It's a funny poem.

   ○ **B.** The poem is about how a person feels.

   ○ **C.** All the lines of the poem are very short.

116 Reading Poetry   Copying is Illegal.   Measuring Up to the OH Learning Outcomes • Reading

How to Write a Short Response

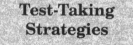

What's Expected on the Test?

On the Ohio Proficiency Test, first you read a selection and answer multiple-choice questions. You learned how to do this in the last group of lessons. Then you will respond to a short-answer question. That is what you will learn now.

In a short-answer response, you don't choose from answers that someone else has written. You have to create an answer on your own. Usually, your answer should be one or two sentences long. To plan your answer, return to the poem one or more times. That will help you understand the poem and find details.

Test-Taking Strategies

Read the Question Carefully

Does the question ask, "How does the owl feel about the pussycat?" or, "How does the pussycat feel about the owl?" There might be a big difference! That's why you should make sure not to misread the question. You might underline key words in the question as an aid.

Be Complete

Answer the whole question, not just part of it. Give details if the question asks for details. Some questions ask you to say more than one thing. Make sure you answer each part of the question.

Be Clear

Write clearly and fully, so that the person scoring the test will understand what you're saying. Use specific words. Write complete sentences. For example, instead of, "Go in a boat," you might write, "The owl and the pussycat sail to sea together in a boat."

Be Accurate

Spell names of characters and places correctly. If you mention a date or time, make sure you get it right. Check details by going back to the poem. Make sure all your facts are correct.

Reread Your Answer

Reread your answer to make sure you really said what you thought you said. That way, you can catch the mistake if you accidentally wrote, "The pussycat plays guitar," instead of, "The owl plays guitar."

Go on to the next page

Lesson 7

How to Write a Short Response

Directions Use those strategies in reading the following poem. Use the questions on the side to help you understand the poem. Then answer the short-answer question.

1 **The Camel's Complaint**
—*Charles Edward Carryl*

"Canary-birds feed on sugar and seed,
    Parrots have crackers to crunch;
And, as for the poodles, they tell me the noodles
    Have chickens and cream for their lunch.

2
      But there's never a question
      About MY digestion-
ANYTHING does for me!

"Cats, you're aware, can repose in a chair,
    Chickens can roost upon rails;
Puppies are able to sleep in a stable,
    And oysters can slumber in pails.
      But no one supposes
      A poor Camel dozes—
ANY PLACE does for me!

3

"Lambs are inclosed where it's never exposed,
    Coops are constructed for hens;
4
Kittens are treated to houses well heated,
    And pigs are protected by pens.
      But a Camel comes handy
      Wherever it's sandy—
ANYWHERE does for me!
"People would laugh if you rode a giraffe,

1 What **prediction** can you make based on the poem's title?

2 What three animal **pictures** are **formed** by the first four lines of the poem?

3 **Summarize** the main point of the second stanza.

4 **Check your understanding**: What is the camel saying about lambs and hens?

GUIDE FOR READING THE POEM AND THE QUESTION

GUIDED QUESTIONS

Or mounted the back of an ox;
It's nobody's habit to ride on a rabbit,
Or try to bestraddle a fox.
But as for a Camel, he's
Ridden by families-
ANY LOAD does for me!

"A snake is as round as a hole in the ground,
And weasels are wavy and sleek;
And no alligator could ever be straighter
Than lizards that live in a creek.
But a Camel's all lumpy
And bumpy and humpy-
ANY SHAPE does for me!"

Sample Short-Answer Question
1. What is the camel complaining about?

_____

_____

_____

_____

5 **Check your understanding**: What does "bestraddle a fox" mean?

6 What sounds **rhyme** at the ends of the fifth and sixth lines of this stanza?

7 **Confirm your prediction**: Is the poem about what you guessed it would be about?

8 **Compare and contrast**: How is the shape of a camel different from the shapes of snakes, weasels, and lizards?

9 In each stanza, the camel has a different complaint. How are the complaints related? **Connect** those **important ideas** in the poem.

10 You're not a camel. But have you ever felt something similar to what this camel feels? **Link** the camel's **ideas to your own experience and knowledge.**

Go on to the next page ➡

 **Directions** Write your answer to the short-answer question on the lines provided above.

Self Evaluation

Ask yourself
- How complete is my answer?
- How much understanding of the poem does my answer show?
- Is my answer detailed enough?
- Is my answer clearly written?

 Measuring Up to the OH Learning Outcomes • Reading

Lesson 8 — How Your Answer Will Be Evaluated

To evaluate your short-answer response, teachers will use a **rubric**. A rubric is a list of grading guidelines. It spells out the criteria for grading—the things the teacher should look for. The teacher will match your answer against the rubric.

Your answer will be scored on a scale of 0-2. Getting a 2 means you gave an excellent, top-notch answer.

Short-Answer Rubric

2	• Is complete and appropriate • Demonstrates a thorough understanding of the poem • Indicates logical reasoning and conclusions • Is accurate, relevant, comprehensive, and detailed

1	• Is partially appropriate • Contains minor flaws in reasoning or neglects to address some aspect of the item or question • Is mostly accurate and relevant but lacks comprehensiveness • Demonstrates an incomplete understanding of the poem or demonstrates an inability to make coherent meaning from the poem

0	• Shows no understanding of the poem or fails to respond to the question

Go on to the next page

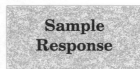
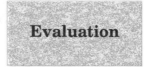
Sample Response

1. What is the camel complaining about?

　　The camel is complaining about how hard his life is. As far as being fed, being rested, being sheltered, and being ridden on, lots of other animals have it better than the camel—and even as far as the shape of his body, the camel feels poorly treated. Other animals get treatment they like, but the camel has to accept "ANYTHING."

Evaluation

　　This is a 2 response. It shows an understanding of the basic point, that the camel is complaining about his hard life. It is packed with details, and even quotes a key word from the poem. It is also a well-written, clear answer.

Activity

Directions Reread your response to the short-answer question. On the lines below, evaluate your answer. Use the rubric.

_____

_____

_____

_____

_____

Measuring Up to the OH Learning Outcomes • Reading

When you compare two things, you say how they are alike. For example, a peach and a plum are alike in that they are both fruits.

When you contrast two things, you say how they are different. For example, a peach and a plum are different in that plums have a more sour taste.

Comparison and contrast are used a lot in poetry. If a poet compares the subject to something unusual, it shows readers a new way of seeing the subject.

The comparisons used in poetry are often figurative. (You have already learned about figurative language in Lesson 2.) The kind of figurative comparison that is easiest to spot is the simile. A simile uses *like*, *as*, or other linking words that signal a comparison. For example, a famous simile is, "My love is like a red, red rose." That's figurative because the speaker's beloved is not really a rose. He's comparing two unlike things—a person and a flower. It's a simile because he uses the word *like*.

Go on to the next page

A. Directions Read the following poem and answer the questions.

City, City
—*Marci Ridlon*

I

City, city,
Wrong and bad,
Looms above me
When I'm sad,
Throws its shadow
On my care,
Sheds its poison
In my air,
Pounds me with its
Noisy fist,
Sprays me with its
Sooty mist.
Till, with sadness
On my face,
I long to live
Another place.

Measuring Up to the OH Learning Outcomes • Reading

Activity continued

II

City, city,
Golden-clad,
Shines around me
When I'm glad
Lifts me with its
Strength and height,
Fills me with its
Sound and sight,
Takes me to its
Crowded heart,
Holds me so I
Won't depart.
Till, with gladness
On my face,
I wouldn't live
Another place.

1. What is the city being compared to in the lines, "Pounds me with its/ Noisy fist?"

   _____

2. What is the city being compared to in the phrase, "Shines around me?"

   _____

Go on to the next page

Activity continued

3. What is figurative about the lines, "Holds me so I won't depart?"

_____

_____

4. Is the expression, "I long to live/ Another place" figurative? Explain.

_____

_____

5. What is the most important difference between Stanza I and Stanza II?

_____

_____

B. Directions Read the following poem and answer the questions.

Some People
—Rachel Field

Isn't it strange some people make
You feel so tired inside,
Your thoughts begin to shrivel up
Like leaves all brown and dried!

But when you're with some other ones,
It's stranger still to find
Your thoughts as thick as fireflies
All shiny in your mind!

Activity continued

1. What is the simile in the first stanza? What is being compared to what?

_____

_____

2. What is the simile in the second stanza? What is being compared to what?

_____

_____

3. What is figurative about the linc, "Your thoughts begin to shrivel up?"

_____

_____

4. What is the most important difference between the first stanza and the second stanza?

_____

_____

5. State one way in which the two stanzas are alike.

_____

_____

Go on to the next page ▷

1. Which of the following is a simile about the city?

◯ **A.** The city is huge.

◯ **C.** The city is a fading flower.

◯ **C.** The city is like a storm.

2. In "Some People," which of the following does the speaker NOT compare people's thoughts to?

◯ **A.** fireflies

◯ **B.** shiny things

◯ **C.** autumn leaves

3. Compare and contrast the poems "City, City" and "Some People." State one way in which they are alike. State one way in which they are different.

_____

_____

_____

_____

_____

Measuring Up to the OH Learning Outcomes • Reading

A problem is a difficulty. It's something that makes a task hard to do. For example, understanding poetry might be a problem for you.

A solution is the way to get over the difficulty. It's what makes the person succeed at the task. For example, you might discover that when you read a poem two or three times, you understand it much better than when you only read it once. That's one solution to the problem.

Solving Problems

To solve a problem, first you need to understand what the problem is. Then, you need to think of possible ways to solve it. You need to try different ways and find the one that works. Some of the ways you try may not work. That means you need to keep trying other ways.

Problems in Poems

How can a poem show problems and solutions? In some poems, a character faces a problem. The character may be the speaker or someone else. Or, a poem might make the reader think about problems he or she faces in real life. A poem can sometimes help a reader solve a real-life problem.

Activity   Directions   Read the following poem and answer the questions.

Mother Doesn't Want a Dog
—Judith Viorst

Mother doesn't want a dog.
Mother says they smell,
And never sit when you say sit,
Or even when you yell.
And when you come home late at night
And there is ice and snow,
You have to go back out because
The dumb dog has to go.

Mother doesn't want a dog.
Mother says they shed,
And always let the strangers in
And bark at friends instead,
And do disgraceful things on rugs,
And track mud on the floor,
And flop upon your bed at night
And snore their doggy snore.

Mother doesn't want a dog.
She's making a mistake.
Because, more than a dog, I think,
She will not want this snake.

130 Reading Poetry   Copying is Illegal.   Measuring Up to the OH Learning Outcomes • Reading

Activity continued

1. The title of the poem tells about the problem in the poem. What is the problem?

_____

_____

2. Whose problem is it, and why?

_____

_____

_____

_____

3. State three problems that the poem mentions about dogs.

_____

_____

4. What solution does the speaker have for the main problem?

_____

_____

5. How might this solution lead to a new problem?

_____

_____

Go on to the next page

Apply to the Test

1. Where is the speaker's solution to the problem stated?

    ○ **A.** in the title

    ○ **B.** in the first line of the poem

    ○ **C.** in the last two lines of the poem

2. What is one broad, general problem the poem hints at? (It is not stated in the poem.)

    ○ **A.** the problem of what to do when it snows

    ○ **B.** the problem of what to do when parent and child don't agree

    ○ **C.** the problem of how to avoid ever making a mistake

3. Do you think the speaker's solution to the problem is a good one? Explain, giving specific details.

    _____

    _____

    _____

    _____

    _____

Vivid Verbs

A **verb** is a word that shows an action or a state of being. A **vivid verb** is a verb that describes its action very clearly, in a fresh or exciting way.

A vivid verb creates a strong, specific picture of the action in your mind. For example, *go* is an action verb. But it isn't very vivid. There are umpteen different ways of going. When you read the verb *go*, the mental picture in your mind is probably pretty fuzzy. Do you picture going fast, going slow, going far, not going far? Do you picture hopping, skipping, running, walking, riding in a plane? The verb *go* might cover any of those.

Hop is a more vivid verb than *go*. When you read *hop*, you're not going to picture walking or skipping or riding in a plane. And you'll probably picture just about the right speed.

Good poets usually use vivid verbs rather than fuzzy, vague verbs. Poets want to create clear pictures in your mind. And they want to show how good they are at finding new ways of saying things!

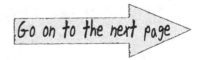

Go on to the next page

Activity

Directions Read the following poem and answer the questions.

The Brook
—Alfred Tennyson

I come from haunts of coot and hern,
    I make a sudden sally,
And sparkle out among the fern,
    To bicker down a valley.

By thirty hills I hurry down,
    Or slip between the ridges,
By twenty thorps,[1] a little town,
    And half a hundred bridges.

Till last by Philip's farm I flow
    To join the brimming river,
For men may come and men may go,
    But I go on forever.

I chatter over stony ways,
    In little sharps and trebles,[2]
I bubble into eddying bays,
    I babble on the pebbles.

With many a curve my banks I fret
    By many a field and fallow,
And many a fairy foreland set
    With willow-weed and mallow.

I chatter, chatter, as I flow
    To join the brimming river,
For men may come and men may go,
    But I go on forever.

I wind about and in and out,
    With here a blossom sailing,
And here and there a lusty trout,
    And here and there a grayling.

And here and there a foamy flake
    Upon me, as I travel
With many a silvery water-break
    Above the golden gravel.

---

[1]**thorps:** hamlets, or little towns.
[2]**sharps and trebles:** musical sounds

And draw them all along, and flow
    To join the brimming river,
For men may come and men may go,
    But I go on forever.

I steal by lawns and grassy plots,
    I slide by hazel covers;
I move the sweet forget-me-nots
    That grow for happy lovers.

I slip, I slide, I gloom, I glance,
    Among my skimming swallows;
I make the netted sunbeam dance
    Against my sandy swallows.

I murmur under moon and stars
    In brambly wilderness;
I linger by my shingly bars,
    I loiter round my cresses;

And out again I curve and flow
    To join the brimming river,
For men may come and men may go,
    But I go on forever.

Go on to the next page

Activity continued

1. The "I" in this poem is the brook. The first two lines tell you that the brook comes "from the haunts of coot and hern," which are two types of birds that live near or on the water. Look at the next two lines. What is the meaning of the verbs *sparkle* and *bicker* in these lines?

_____

_____

2. Notice the three vivid verbs in the fourth stanza. What do the verbs *chatter*, *bubble*, and *babble* mean in these lines?

_____

_____

3. Find the vivid verb *steal* in the tenth stanza. What does this verb mean?

_____

_____

4. Look at the eleventh stanza. Which verb do you find to be the most vivid? Explain your answer.

_____

_____

5. Look at the last two stanzas. Which verb do you find to be the most vivid? Explain your answer.

_____

_____

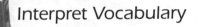

Apply to the Test

1. Which of the following is a vivid verb?

   ○ **A.** stalking

   ○ **B.** tidbits

   ○ **C.** whiskery

2. Which of the following phrases contains a vivid verb?

   ○ **A.** A carroty lettucey cabbagey luncheon

   ○ **B.** He munched on taco chips.

   ○ **C.** Here's a banana for you!

3. What happens in the poem's last stanza? Explain your answer. Use vivid verbs in your response.

   _____

   _____

   _____

   _____

   _____

   _____

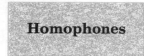

 **Skill Builder**

Homophones

Homophones are words that sound the same but have different meanings. Usually they have different spellings, too. Here are some examples of homophones:

I (a person, me)
eye (the part of the body that sees)

son (male child)
sun (our star)

know (to have knowledge of something)
no (a negative)

When you hear someone say the sound of *I/eye*, you use the words around it to tell you which meaning is meant. You use what you already know. If someone says, "I have something in my eye," you can tell that the first /[long-i]/ sound means the person talking and the second /[long-i]/ sound means the part of the body that sees.

When you read, both the spelling and the context help you find the meaning.

Activity

Directions Read the poem and answer the questions.

There's Always Weather
—Langston Hughes

There's always weather, weather,
Whether we like it or not.
Some days are nice and sunny,
Sunny and bright and hot.

There's always weather, weather,
Whether we like it or don't.
Sometimes so cold and cloudy!
Will it soon snow, or won't?

If days were always just the same,
Out-of-doors would be so tame—
Never a wild and windy day,
Never a stormy sky of gray.

I'm glad there's weather, whether,
Dark days, then days full of sun.
Summer and fall and winter—
Weather is so much fun!

Go on to the next page

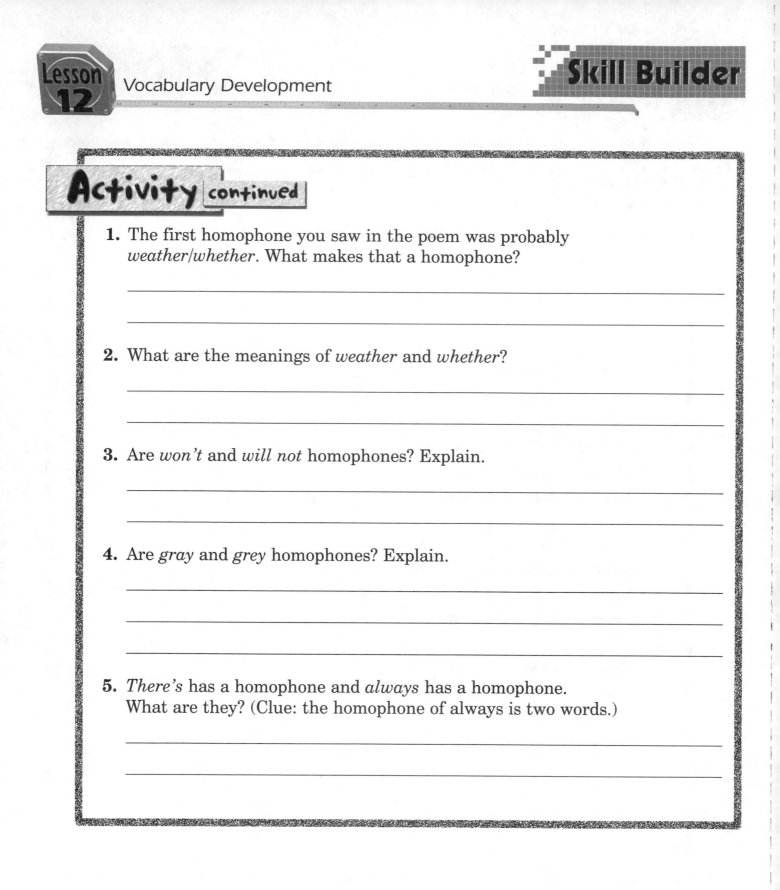
Activity continued

1. The first homophone you saw in the poem was probably
   weather/whether. What makes that a homophone?

   _____

   _____

2. What are the meanings of *weather* and *whether*?

   _____

   _____

3. Are *won't* and *will not* homophones? Explain.

   _____

   _____

4. Are *gray* and *grey* homophones? Explain.

   _____

   _____

   _____

5. *There's* has a homophone and *always* has a homophone.
   What are they? (Clue: the homophone of always is two words.)

   _____

   _____

Apply to the Test

1. Which of the following is a pair of homophones?

○ **A.** days/daze

○ **B.** say/says

○ **C.** like/lice

2. Which of the following is NOT a pair of homophones?

○ **A.** so/sew

○ **B.** be/bee

○ **C.** full/fall

3. Write two sentences about the weather. In each sentence, use a word that has a homophone. Underline those words. Then, write the homophone of each underlined word. DON'T use *weather* and *whether*! Look through this lesson for homophones you can use.

_____

_____

_____

_____

Directions: Read the selection and answer the questions.

The Ants at the Olympics
Richard Digance

At last year's Jungle Olympics,
the Ants were completely outclassed.
In fact, from an entry of sixty-two teams,
the Ants came their usual last.

They didn't win one single medal.
Not that that's a surprise.
The reason was not lack of trying,
but more their unfortunate size.

While the cheetahs won most of the sprinting
and the hippos won putting the shot,
the Ants tried sprinting but couldn't,
and tried to put but could not.

It was sad for the ants 'cause they're sloggers.
They turn out for every event.
With their shorts and their bright orange tee-shirts,
their athletes are proud they are sent.

They came last at the high jump and hurdles,
which they say they'd have won, but they fell.
They came last in the four hundred meters
and last in the swimming as well.

They came last in the long-distance running,
though they say they might have come first.
And they might if the other sixty-one teams
hadn't put in a finishing burst.

But each year they turn up regardless.
They're popular in the parade.
The other teams whistle and cheer them,
aware of the journeys they've made.

For the Jungle Olympics in August,
they have to set off New Year's Day.
They didn't arrive the year before last.
They set off but went the wrong way.

So long as they try there's a reason.
After all, it's only a sport.
They'll be back next year to bring up the rear,
and that's an encouraging thought.

1. What is the Ants' main problem at the Jungle Olympics?

   ○ **A.** The other animals don't notice them.

   ○ **B.** The cheetahs are faster than they are.

   ○ **C.** Their tiny size works against them.

2. How do the Ants solve the problem of needing a long time to get to the Jungle Olympics?

   ○ **A.** They ride on the backs of the hippos.

   ○ **B.** They start out very early.

   ○ **C.** They live at the Olympics—they never leave.

Go On

3. Compared to the other animals, the Ants probably

○ **A.** try harder

○ **B.** win more medals

○ **C.** are careless

4. Which is a more vivid way of saying *running*?

○ **A.** trying

○ **B.** finishing

○ **C.** sprinting

5. In the line, "But each year they turn up regardless,"
regardless means

○ **A.** often

○ **B.** early

○ **C.** anyway

6. How do the other animals feel about the Ants, and why?

_____

_____

_____

_____

144 Reading Poetry   Copying is Illegal.   Measuring Up to the OH Learning Outcomes • Reading

What's Expected on the Test?

Another type of question found on the Ohio Proficiency Test is the extended-response question. An extended response is usually several sentences long. It contains more detail than the short response. Like a short response, it asks you to think for yourself. It may ask you to support your ideas with details from the selection.

An extended response question may ask you to retell what is in the selection. This means that you should put information or events into your own words.

Another kind of extended response you might be asked for is a personal response. This means that you should connect what you read to your own life and experience.

An extended response question may also ask you to write critically about a selection. This means that you should think about what is good or bad about the selection. In thinking critically, you must back up your judgment with evidence.

Test-Taking Strategies

Read the Question Carefully

It's easy to skip over words and misunderstand directions on a test. A question might ask you about a poem's **rhythms** and you might accidentally read that word as **rhymes**. This can cost you a lot of points. But you can avoid making this kind of mistake. Read the question at least twice. Ask yourself: What are they asking for?

Look for Key Words

Certain words in test questions give you signals about how to focus your answer. For example, if the question asks you to **compare and contrast**, that's a signal telling you to find ways in which two things are alike or unlike. Another question about the same selection might ask you to **retell**. That's a signal that you should put the poem's events into your own words.

Stay on Target

Focus on the topic of the question. Don't let your words wander off course. Make sure that every part of your answer really answers the question.

Go on to the next page

Answer All Parts of the Question

In an extended response, you may need to do more than one thing. For example, a question may say, "How are music and dance important in 'The Owl and the Pussycat'?" If you just write about the music the owl plays and sings, that's only part of the answer. You forgot to write about the wedding dance at the end of the poem! Ask yourself: Have I left anything out? Have I answered everything they asked?

Using Connecting Words and Phrases

Remember that one of your goals is to make your answer clear to the person scoring it. Connecting words show your reader how one of your ideas leads to the next. Little words like *because*, *since*, *so*, *thus*, *first*, *second*, *next*, *last*, and *afterward* can make a big difference.

146 Reading Poetry   Copying is Illegal.   Measuring Up to the OH Learning Outcomes • Reading

READING GUIDE

GUIDED QUESTIONS

Directions Read the following poem. Use the questions at the right to help you use reading strategies. Plan an answer to the extended-response question. Write your answer on the lines provided.

1 **Homework**

　　—Russell Hoban

Homework sits on top of Sunday,
2 squashing Sunday flat.
Homework has the smell of Monday,
3 homework's very fat.
Heavy books and piles of paper, answers I don't know.
Sunday evening's almost finished,
4 now I'm going to go
Do my homework in the kitchen.
5 Maybe just a snack,
Then I'll sit right down and start as soon as I run back
6 For some chocolate sandwich cookies.
Then I'll really do

1 **Make** one or two **predictions** about the poem based on its title.

2 What is the **figurative language** in the first line? What does it mean?

3 There's more **figurative language** in the second line: "Homework has the smell of Monday," and "homework's very fat." **Link** these **ideas to your own experience and knowledge** to sense what they mean.

4 Notice the **rhymes** and **rhythms** in the poem so far. Keep noticing them as you read. How would you describe them?

5 **Retell** what the speaker is planning to do.

6 **Make an inference**: how does the speaker feel about doing his homework?

Go on to the next page

READING GUIDE

7 All that homework in a minute.
First I'll see what new
Show they've got on television in the living room.

8 Everybody's laughing there, but misery and gloom

9 And a full refrigerator are where I am at.

10 I'll just have another sandwich.

11 Homework's very fat.

Sample Extended Response Question

1. Describe the problem the speaker is facing and what he is doing about it. Is he solving his problem successfully? Explain why or why not.

_____

_____

_____

_____

_____

GUIDED QUESTIONS

7 **Predict outcomes**: Is he going to do his homework or not?

8 **Form a picture** in your mind of exactly where the speaker is and what he's doing. Describe what you see.

9 **Connect important ideas**: In this poem, what do eating and homework have to do with each other?

10 **Check your understanding**: "Homework's very fat," the speaker says again. Do you see what he means?

11 **Confirm and revise your predictions**: Is he going to do the homework or not?

148   Reading Poetry   Copying is Illegal.   Measuring Up to the OH Learning Outcomes • Reading

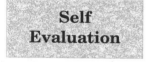

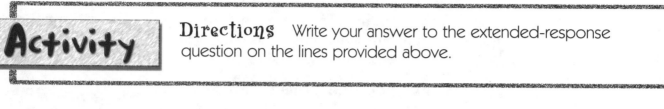

Directions Write your answer to the extended-response question on the lines provided above.

Self Evaluation

Ask yourself
- Does my answer show a solid understanding of the poem?
- Do I address all the aspects of the question fully?
- Do I give detailed reasons for my answers?
- Is my thinking logical?
- Do I communicate clearly?

Your answer will be evaluated on a scale of 0–4. Teachers will score the answer using the rubric below. Read the rubric to learn what the scorers will be looking for.

Extended-Response Rubric

4	• Provides extensive evidence of the kind of interpretation called for in the item or question • Is well organized, elaborate, and thorough • Demonstrates a complete understanding of the whole poem as well as how the parts blend to form the whole • Is relevant, comprehensive, and detailed, demonstrating a thorough understanding of the poem • Addresses thoroughly the important elements of the question • Contains logical reasoning and communicates effectively and clearly (A four-point response may go beyond the requirements of the item)

3	• Provides evidence that essential interpretation has been made
	• Is thoughtful and reasonably accurate
	• Indicates an understanding of the concept or item
	• Communicates adequately, and generally reaches reasonable conclusions
	• Contains some combination of the following flaws:
	  ♦ Minor flaws in reasoning or interpretation
	  ♦ Failure to address some aspect of the item or omission of some detail

2	• Is mostly accurate and relevant
	• Contains some combination of the following flaws:
	  • Incomplete evidence of interpretation
	  • Unsubstantiated statements made about the text
	  • Incomplete understanding of the concept or item
	  • Lack of comprehensiveness, faulty reasoning, unclear communication

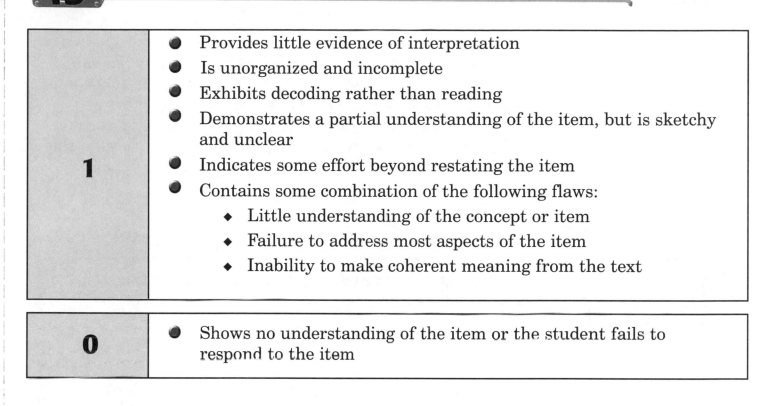

1	● Provides little evidence of interpretation
	● Is unorganized and incomplete
	● Exhibits decoding rather than reading
	● Demonstrates a partial understanding of the item, but is sketchy and unclear
	● Indicates some effort beyond restating the item
	● Contains some combination of the following flaws:
	◆ Little understanding of the concept or item
	◆ Failure to address most aspects of the item
	◆ Inability to make coherent meaning from the text
0	● Shows no understanding of the item or the student fails to respond to the item

 **Question**

1. Describe the problem the speaker is facing and what he is doing about it. Is he solving his problem successfully? Explain why or why not.

 **Answer**

The speaker faces the problem of having to do his homework on Sunday evening, when he doesn't want to. He's trying to get over his problem, but it doesn't seem as if he's doing enough. All he's doing is worrying about his homework and telling himself he has to do it. But actually he's avoiding doing it. He's stalling by looking in the refrigerator, eating, and watching TV. If that's all he's going to do to solve the problem, he's not going to succeed—the homework isn't going to get done. But if eating and watching TV are ways he usually warms up for doing homework, then it's okay. He'll do it in the end. Maybe he always does his homework this way, and it does get finished. On the other hand, maybe he's doing poorly in school, and stalling on his homework is one of the reasons. The poem doesn't show us the outcome.

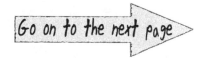

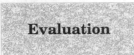
Evaluation

This answer gets a 4, the highest score. It answers all the parts of the question in detail. It describes the speaker's problem and attempted solution, and it evaluates how successful the solution is. The response communicates clearly and readably. It shows a thorough understanding of the poem, and shows that the speaker has thought about the poem's meaning. It goes a little beyond the requirements of the question by addressing possible outcomes of the problem and solution.

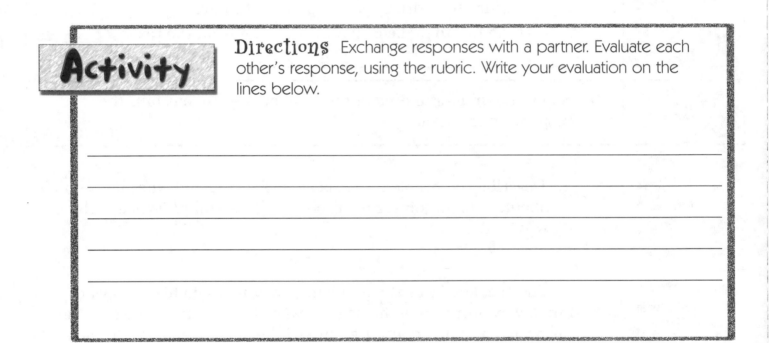

Activity

Directions Exchange responses with a partner. Evaluate each other's response, using the rubric. Write your evaluation on the lines below.

Retelling a poem means putting the poem's contents into your own words. If you can retell what you've read, it's a sign that you understood the poem.

Your retelling won't be a poem. It will be more like a story or an explanation. It should contain

- the subject of the poem
- any important characters and events in the poem
- major ideas and feelings in the poem
- details that illustrate important aspects of the poem

A retelling of a poem may include one or more brief quotations of important or beautiful words or phrases from the poem. These should be in quotation marks. The rest of the retelling should be your own. The retelling should not include minor details.

Autumn Silence
—Katie McAllaster Weaver

Fall shadows
creep up on my driveway.
I try pushing them
away with the thumping
of basketballs against
the house, shouting
sounds of summer
to my friends.

Go on to the next page

But the autumn silence
always wins, and I
sit silently on
the school bus,
humming summer songs, because I
have already
forgotten almost all
the words.

Activity

Directions   Retell the poem.

_____

_____

_____

_____

_____

_____

When you proofread, you read your written work carefully in order to correct any errors. Always proofread your answers to the extended-response questions on the Ohio Proficiency Test. Correct any errors in

- spelling
- punctuation
- grammar
- mechanics (such as capitalization)

Activity

Directions The paragraph below is a retelling of the poem "Autumn Silence." It contains ten errors. Correct all ten.

"Autumn silence" is about how autumn creeps up on you. When you wish it was still "summer." The speaker sees shaddows in her driveway. Their the shadows of autumn. She tries playing basketball and shouting to her friends so she can feel like it's still summer? But then she has to go to school. Doesnt want to. She sits silently on the bus humming summer songs but she can't remember the words of the songs. That's how far away summer alredy is.

Directions: Read the selection and answer the questions.

Eat-it-all Elaine

by Kaye Starbird

I went away last August
To summer camp in Maine,
And there I met a camper
Called Eat-it-all Elaine.
Although Elaine was quiet,
She liked to cause a stir
By acting out the nickname
Her camp-mates gave to her.

The day of our arrival
At Cabin Number Three
When girls kept coming over
To greet Elaine and me,
She took a piece of Kleenex
And calmly chewed it up,
Then strolled outside the cabin
And ate a buttercup.

Elaine, from that day forward,
Was always in command.
On hikes, she'd eat some birch-bark.
On swims, she'd eat some sand.
At meals, she'd swallow prunte-pits
And never have a pain,
While everyone around her
Would giggle, "Oh, Elaine!"

One morning, berry-picking,
A bug was in her pail,
And though we thought for certain
Her appetite would fail,
Elaine said, "Hmm, a stinkbug."
And while we murmured, "Ooh,"
She ate her pail of berries
And ate the stinkbug, too.

The night of Final Banquet
When counselors were handing
Awards to different children
Whom they believed outstanding,
To every *thinking* person
At summer camp in Maine
The Most Outstanding Camper
Was Eat-it-all Elaine.

1. How are the words *stinkbug*, *nickname*, and *buttercup* alike?

   ○ **A.** They rhyme.

   ○ **B.** They are compound words.

   ○ **C.** They are only used in poetry.

2. Why is Elaine called Eat-it-all?

   ○ **A.** She always finishes her meal.

   ○ **B.** She always asks for seconds.

   ○ **C.** She eats things people usually don't eat.

3. Who is "I" in this poem?

   ○ **A.** A girl who met Elaine at camp.

   ○ **B.** Elaine's mother.

   ○ **C.** The counselor who named Elaine "Most Outstanding Camper."

Go On

4. In this poem, what does "every *thinking* person" mean?

   ○ **A.** every single person

   ○ **B.** every outstanding camper

   ○ **C.** everyone except the counselors

5. Which of these pairs of lines from the poem most clearly explains Elaine's behavior?

   ○ **A.** "And there I met a camper/ Called Eat-it-all Elaine."

   ○ **B.** "Although Elaine was quiet,/ She liked to cause a stir"

   ○ **C.** "She took a piece of Kleenex/ And calmly chewed it up"

6. Suppose it is the day after camp ends. Elaine is back home. What will happen to her? Why do you think so?

   _____

   _____

   _____

   _____

7. Retell the poem in your own words.

   _____

   _____

   _____

   _____

   _____

   _____

   _____

   _____

Measuring Up to the OH Learning Outcomes • Reading

Choose Materials

1. Go to the school library or public library and find the poetry section for young people. Look through lots of books of poetry. Some of them may be books by a single author. Others may be anthologies—collections of poems by many authors. Find five poems that express happiness and five that express sadness. Write the titles and authors on the lines below. (Extra challenge: Can you find both kinds of poems by the same person?)

Poems of Happiness   Poems of Sadness

_____   _____

_____   _____

_____   _____

_____   _____

_____   _____

2. Below are ten topics. Choose your favorite topic and look for poems about it. Jot down the names of at least five poems that you find on the topic. Read two of the poems thoroughly. You might want to share your findings with classmates.

vacation	school	animals
parents	monsters	world problems
friendship	hopes for the future	
plants	nonsense	

Reading Activity

Make a personal anthology of poems. Gather your favorite poems, and put them in a folder or staple them together. Think about what order to put them in, such as by date of publication or by subject. Give your anthology a title. Create a cover, including the title, your name as editor, and a picture or design. Draw illustrations for individual poems if you wish. Write an Introduction. In the Introduction, talk about why you chose these poems. Make a Table of Contents. At the end of the book, write a List of Poets. Include some brief information about each poet, such as date and place of birth, date of death (if applicable), where the poet lived, how the poet made his or her living, and titles of the poet's major works.

Share your anthology with your class, and keep it for your own memories. Keep in mind that most of the poems will probably be copyrighted by their authors. Your anthology is just for fun—you can't sell it.

Speaking and Listening Activity

Give a poetry reading for your class. Choose three to six poems that you really like. Read them aloud. Read naturally and with appropriate expression. After you've read all the poems, lead a discussion about what you and your classmates liked, or didn't like, in the poems. Then listen as other students give poetry readings.

Chapter 3 Reading Nonfiction

Does This Sound Familiar?

- You are taking a vacation. You look for a travel guide to give you information about your trip.

- You just saw a movie about the Amistad. You go to the Internet to find out more about this event?

- You just received a ten-speed bicycle. You read the manual to find out how the gear shift works?

Nonfiction Is All Around You!

If you hunger for information, you probably read a lot of nonfiction. You can find nonfiction in libraries, in bookstores, in magazines, in newspapers, and on the Internet. You can watch nonfiction as documentaries on television and listen to it as news shows on the radio.

Warm Up

Directions Information is all around us. Go on an information scavenger hunt to find each of the following:

1. the largest library in your community
   Name:_____
   Location:_____

2. the nearest museum
   Name:_____
   Location:_____

3. the best place to find information about city history
   Name:_____
   Location:_____

4. the best place to find information about state history
   Name:_____
   Location:_____

5. the nearest planetarium
   Name:_____
   Location:_____

Nonfiction contains information about the real world. It provides facts about real-life things, real-life people, and real-life events. Nonfiction may be about science or social studies or health. It may be about math. It may even tell you facts about authors and the books they have written. The most important thing to remember is that nonfiction is not made-up. It tells you information about people who actually live, places that really do exist, and events that really happened.

Forms of Nonfiction

Print	**Non-print**	**Electronic Media**
biographies	newscasts	CD-Rom encyclopedias
reference books	documentaries	CD-Rom dictionaries
magazines	historical movies	websites
newspapers	television biographies	Internet
brochures	historic villages	e-mail

 **Special Text Features**

Often, you know nonfiction as soon as you see it. Usually it looks different from fiction. It has special text features that include:

Subheads: Subheads provide a title for sections. Sometimes the subheads are in boldface. Sometimes they are in all capital letters. Sometimes they are even questions.

Graphic Aids: Maps, graphs, charts, and illustrations present the information in a visual form.

Captions: Captions are the words under the graphic aids. They tell you about what you are seeing.

Definitions: Nonfiction may include special vocabulary. Often these special words are defined in the text.

Type Treatments: Words or ideas may be highlighted by using special type treatments. These include boldface, italics, all capital letters, small capital letters, and color.

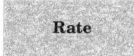

Purpose

When you read for information, you may want to

- **find** specific facts or data that answer your questions about the topic
- **understand** why events happened or what are the effects of certain situations
- gain enough information to help you **solve problems** or figure things out
- simply **enjoy** what you are reading

Rate

How quickly or slowly should you read nonfiction? Ask yourself two questions: How difficult is the selection? What is my purpose for reading it?

- Read **slowly and carefully** when you
  - ◆ are studying for a test
  - ◆ see a lot of difficult words
  - ◆ need to take time to think about the ideas
- **Skim**, or glance through the selection without reading every word, when you
  - ◆ are deciding whether or not to read it
  - ◆ want to get a general idea of what it is about
- **Scan**, or let your eyes search for specific information, when you
  - ◆ are hunting for specific facts
  - ◆ are looking for names or dates
  - ◆ need only some of the information in the selection
- Read at a **comfortable rate** when you are
  - ◆ reading for enjoyment
  - ◆ the selection seems easy to read and to understand

Activity

Directions Think about all the things you have read and listened to for information. Then brainstorm to create a list of as many forms of nonfiction as you can. Stretch your mind. Of course, you will include books. Also try to include some unusual items. List labels on products. List information on the back of cereal boxes. Include schedules on airport monitors. Include information on place mats in restaurants, for example. Share your list with your classmates.

Print	
Non-Print	
Electronic Media	

How do you read nonfiction effectively? How do you make sure you understand the meaning? The following strategies and skills will help you be successful.

When you read,

Summarize

Pause to summarize from time to time as you read. A summary gives the main points. It leaves out all the extra details. When you summarize, you focus on what is important.

Graphic Aids

Use graphic aids to help you understand the meaning. Graphic aids include tables, charts, diagrams, maps, and illustrations.

Retell

Pause to retell, or put information in your own words. This will help you check that you truly understand what you have read.

Vocabulary

You may not know the meaning of all the words. Check for context clues. Sometimes the author defines the word. If the word isn't defined, look at the topic of the passage and the other words surrounding the unknown words. They may provide clues that help you figure out the meaning. If context doesn't help, use your dictionary.

 Measuring Up to the OH Learning Outcomes • Reading

READING GUIDE

GUIDED QUESTIONS

Directions Use the questions in the right-hand column to guide your reading.

1 *from . . .* **If You Traveled West in a Covered Wagon**
—*Ellen Levine*

One hundred and fifty years ago there was no railroad that went all across the country. There were no cars or buses or airplanes. The only way to travel across the country was to ride a horse, or if you went with your family, to travel in a covered wagon.

2
3 In the 1840s and 1850s, thousands of people traveled west. So if you lived at that time, there was a chance you might have traveled in a covered wagon.

What was the Oregon Territory?

In the 1840s the Oregon Territory was made up of the land that is now the states of Oregon, Washington, Idaho, and parts of Montana and Wyoming.

Back then nobody knew if the Oregon Territory was going to be part of America or if it was going to be part of England. Both countries had built forts in the territory. At the forts, trappers and Indians sold animal furs and skins, such as beaver, marten, and muskrat, and bought tools and supplies.

4 America and England agreed that Oregon would belong to the country that could get more of its people living in the new land. So to make Oregon part of America, many Americans had to go there to live. Oregon finally became a state in 1859.

Why did some people want to travel all the way to Oregon?

Back in the 1840s, you heard about far away places by reading the newspaper or hearing stories told by visitors who came from distant places. This is how people learned of the land on the other side—the west side—of the Rocky Mountains. That land was called

1 **Topic** The title tells you the topic, or what the article is about. What is the topic?

2 **Details** When did the events in this article happen?

3 **Picture** Picture traveling this way. What hardships do you think people faced?

4 **Reasons** This paragraph gives you a reason why so many Americans had to travel to the Oregon Territory. What is it?

Go on to the next page ⟹

READING GUIDE

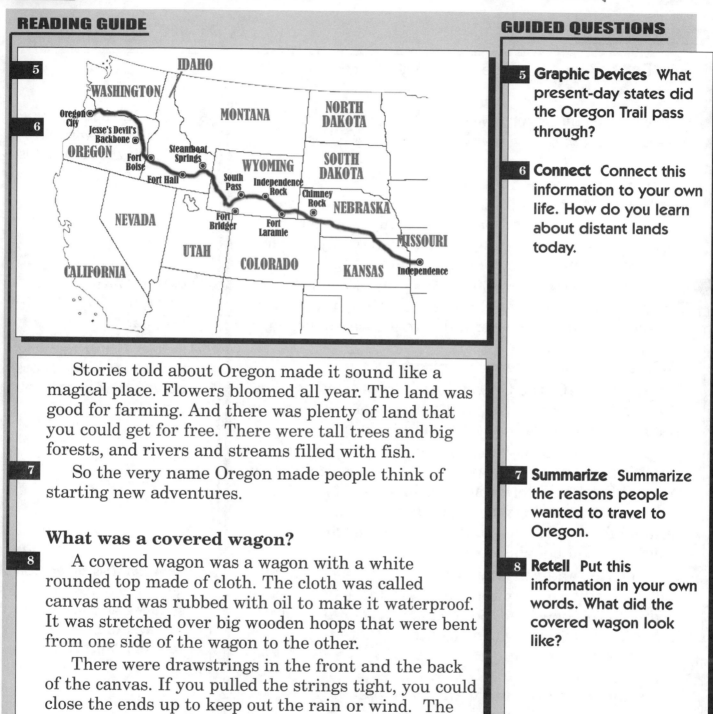

GUIDED QUESTIONS

5 **Graphic Devices** What present-day states did the Oregon Trail pass through?

6 **Connect** Connect this information to your own life. How do you learn about distant lands today.

Stories told about Oregon made it sound like a magical place. Flowers bloomed all year. The land was good for farming. And there was plenty of land that you could get for free. There were tall trees and big forests, and rivers and streams filled with fish.

7 So the very name Oregon made people think of starting new adventures.

7 **Summarize** Summarize the reasons people wanted to travel to Oregon.

What was a covered wagon?

8 A covered wagon was a wagon with a white rounded top made of cloth. The cloth was called canvas and was rubbed with oil to make it waterproof. It was stretched over big wooden hoops that were bent from one side of the wagon to the other.

There were drawstrings in the front and the back of the canvas. If you pulled the strings tight, you could close the ends up to keep out the rain or wind. The canvas could also be rolled up on the long sides, so that you could get a breeze on a hot day.

The bottom part of the covered wagon looked like an ordinary wagon with one difference: The front wheels were smaller than the back wheels. That made it easier to make sharp turns.

8 **Retell** Put this information in your own words. What did the covered wagon look like?

READING GUIDE

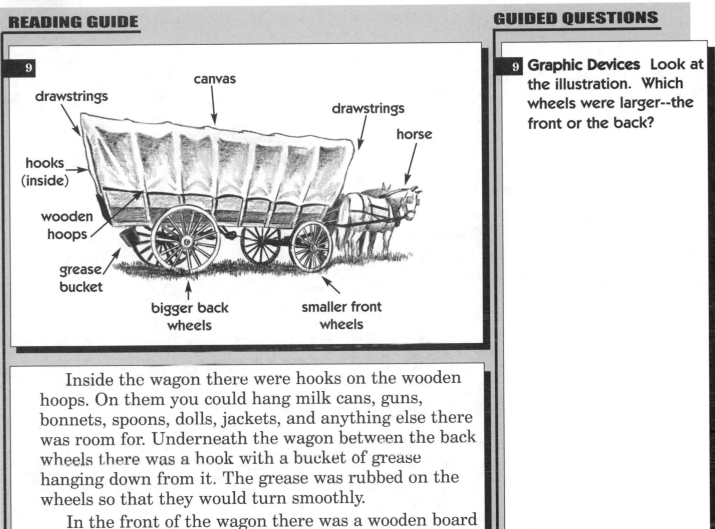

9

drawstrings

canvas

drawstrings

horse

hooks
(inside)

wooden
hoops

grease
bucket

bigger back
wheels

smaller front
wheels

9 **Graphic Devices** Look at the illustration. Which wheels were larger--the front or the back?

Inside the wagon there were hooks on the wooden hoops. On them you could hang milk cans, guns, bonnets, spoons, dolls, jackets, and anything else there was room for. Underneath the wagon between the back wheels there was a hook with a bucket of grease hanging down from it. The grease was rubbed on the wheels so that they would turn smoothly.

In the front of the wagon there was a wooden board to sit on.

The covered wagon was pulled by oxen or mules or horses. Many pioneers used oxen because they were stronger than mules and horses.

10 Covered wagons were also called prairie schooners. Can you guess why?

A schooner is a boat that sails on the seas. The big white canvas cover on the wagon looked like a huge sail. And if the grass was tall enough to hide the wheels, the wagon looked like a big boat sailing across the grassy green waves.

10 **Vocabulary** Use context to figure out the meaning of prairie schooner. Can you picture lines of prairie schooners sailing across the prairies?

What's Expected on the Test?

Some of the selections you will read on the Ohio Proficiency Test will be nonfiction. In this lesson, you will practice answering multiple-choice questions about them.

Test-Taking Strategies

Find Key Words

Look for key words as you read the question. These words tell you exactly what to do. Sometimes key words are printed in capital letters. Words like NOT and EXCEPT tell you to watch out. Don't be tricked.

Read All the Choice First

The choices have letters in front of them. Read all the choices first. Then cross out the choice that seems very wrong. Next, think a little harder to narrow down your choice. Finally, select the one and only answer that fits.

Mark Your Answer

Mark your answer by filling in the circle by the letter of your choice. Fill in only one answer. If you erase, make sure you erase completely. If two letters are marked, then your answer will be marked wrong.

Check Your Answers

It's easy to make careless mistakes. Reread your answers. Make sure they make sense. Check that you filled in the right letter.

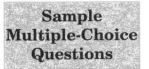

Sample Multiple-Choice Questions

1. How did most families travel to the West in the 1840s and 1850s?

   ○ **A.** by airplane
   ○ **B.** on horseback
   ○ **C.** in covered wagons

2. The United States wanted Americans to move to the Oregon Territory. Which reason best explains why?

   ○ **A.** The East was getting very crowded.
   ○ **B.** America wanted everyone to have their own farmland.
   ○ **C.** To make Oregon part of America, more Americans than English had to live there.

3. All of the following reasons explain why people wanted to travel to the Oregon Territory EXCEPT

   ○ **A.** Everyone already had a covered wagon.
   ○ **B.** There was plenty of land for farming.
   ○ **C.** There was plenty of wildlife for hunting and fishing.

4. Which of the following items best fits in the diagram below.

   ○ **A.** top made of leather
   ○ **B.** frame made of steel
   ○ **C.** wooden board to sit on

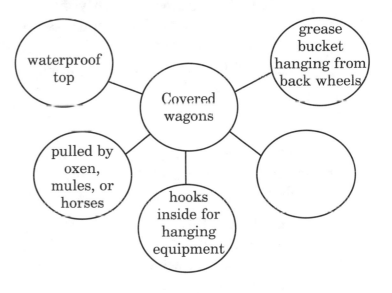

5. The Oregon Territory was made up of land that includes all of the following states EXCEPT

   ○ **A.** California
   ○ **B.** Idaho
   ○ **C.** Washington

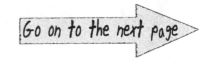
Go on to the next page

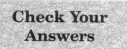
Check Your Answers

1. How did most families travel to the West in the 1840s and 1850s?

   ○ **A. INCORRECT** Airplanes did not exist then.

   ○ **B. INCORRECT** Individuals might travel by horseback. But if you were with your family, most likely you used a covered wagon.

   ● **C. CORRECT** This is the way you would travel.

2. The United States wanted Americans to move to the Oregon Territory. Which reason best explains why?

   ○ **A. INCORRECT** The article does not mention the East being crowded.

   ○ **B. INCORRECT** This is not the reason the *government* wanted people to move there.

   ● **C. CORRECT** America and England agreed that Oregon would belong to the country that could get more of its people living there.

3. All of the following reasons explain why people wanted to travel to the Oregon Territory EXCEPT

   ● **A. CORRECT** Everyone did not have a covered wagon. This is NOT a reason why they wanted to travel to the Oregon Territory.

   ○ **B. INCORRECT** People DID want to go there because there was plenty of land for farming.

   ○ **C. INCORRECT** People DID want to go there because there was plenty of wildlife for hunting and fishing.

4. Which of the following items best fits in the diagram below?

○ **A.** **INCORRECT** The top was made of canvas.

○ **B.** **INCORRECT** The frame was made of wood.

● **C.** **CORRECT** There was a wooden board to sit on.

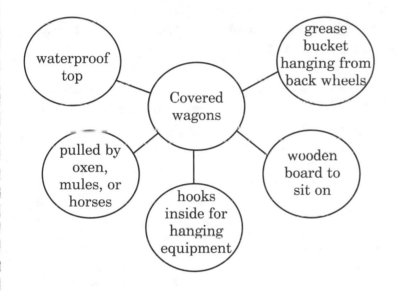

waterproof top

grease bucket hanging from back wheels

Covered wagons

pulled by oxen, mules, or horses

hooks inside for hanging equipment

wooden board to sit on

5. The Oregon Territory is made up of land that includes all of the following states EXCEPT

● **A.** **CORRECT** The land that is now California was NOT part of it.

○ **B.** **INCORRECT** The land that is now Idaho was part of it.

○ **C.** **INCORRECT** The land that is now Washington was part of it.

Compound Words

A compound word is made up of two or more smaller words. For example, the word *nobody* is made up of the words *no* and *body*.

no	+	body	=	nobody

To figure out the meaning of a compound word, first divide it into the smaller words. Look at their meaning. Add these meanings together to form the meaning of the larger word.

For example, the word no means "not any." The word body means "person." By adding together these two meanings, you find that nobody means "not any person."

Activity

A. Directions   Find the compound word in each sentence below. Then draw a line between the two words that make up the compound word. Write its meaning on the line. Check your answer in a dictionary.

1. There were no railroads in the 1840s.

   _____

2. People could not travel by airplane.

   _____

3. People found out about Oregon from the newspapers.

   _____

4. The top was waterproof.

   _____

5. Drawstrings pulled the sides together.

   _____

B. Directions   Try it on your own. Make five compound words using the word *road*.

1. _____   3. _____

2. _____   4. _____

                                          5. _____

A summary presents the most important ideas in a brief form. It leaves out details that are not important.

Directions Reread the article from . . . *If You Traveled West in a Covered Wagon.* Then follow the steps for creating a summary.

1. Reread the first paragraph on page 167. Write a sentence that tells the most important idea.

_____

_____

2. Reread the second paragraph. Write a sentence that tells the most important idea.

_____

_____

3. Reread the passage answering the question "What was the Oregon Territory?" Write the most important idea.

_____

_____

4. Reread the passage answering the question "Why did some people want to travel all the way to Oregon?" Write the most important idea.

_____

_____

5. Reread the passage answering the question "What was a covered wagon." Write the most important idea.

_____

_____

Go on to the next page

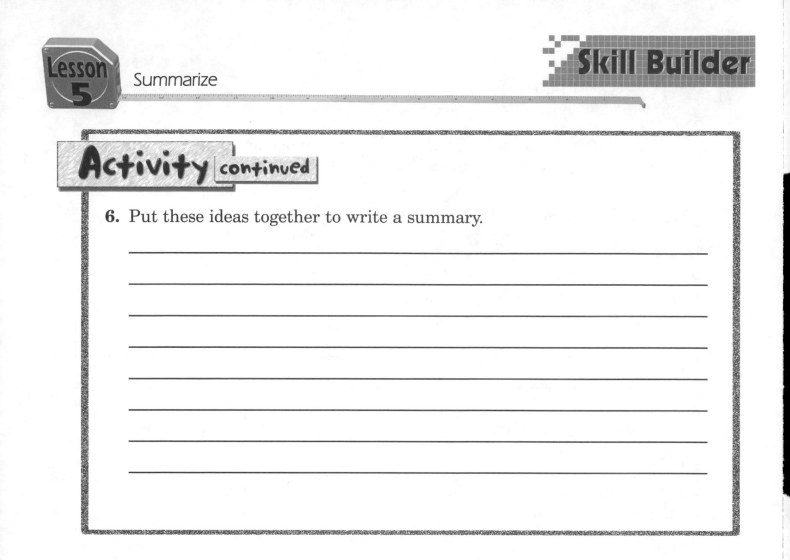

Activity continued

6. Put these ideas together to write a summary.

_____

_____

_____

_____

_____

_____

_____

_____

Apply to the Test

1. Which statement below summarizes the other statements?

○ **A.** A covered wagon had a rounded top made of waterproof cloth.

○ **B.** A covered wagon was well designed.

○ **C.** Drawstrings could be pulled to keep the rain out.

2. Which statement below summarizes the other statements?

○ **A.** People thought that flowers bloomed in Oregon all year round.

○ **B.** The streams were filled with fish.

○ **C.** Oregon sounded like a wonderful place.

A table is a tool for organizing words and numbers. Because it is easy to read, it helps you see the relationship between information.

Look at the table below. Seventeen states became part of the Union from 1800-1860. The table lists the dates in the left-hand column. It lists the names of the states in the right-hand column.

Activity

A. Directions Read the table below. Then answer the questions.

The Expanding United States—1800-1860

Date Entered Union	State
1803	Ohio
1812	Louisiana
1816	Indiana
1817	Mississippi
1818	Illinois
1819	Alabama
1820	Maine
1821	Missouri
1836	Arkansas
1837	Michigan
1845	Florida
1845	Texas
1846	Iowa
1848	Wisconsin
1850	California
1858	Minnesota
1859	Oregon

Go on to the next page

Activity continued

1. What state entered the Union in 1837? _____

2. What state entered the Union in 1803? _____

3. When did Illinois enter the Union? _____

4. When did Oregon enter the Union? _____

5. Which state entered the Union first: Ohio, Indiana, or Michigan?

   _____

B. Directions   Read the table below. Then answer the questions.

Where Are People Living Now?	
STATE	**POPULATION**
CALIFORNIA	33,145,100
FLORIDA	15,111,200
ILLINOIS	12,128,400
INDIANA	5,942,900
NEW YORK	18,196,600
OHIO	11,256,700
OREGON	3,316,200
PENNSYLVANIA	11,994,000
TEXAS	20,044,100
VERMONT	593,700

Population estimates from US Census Bureau, 7/1/99

Activity continued

1. Which state on the table has the largest population?_____

2. What is the population of Oregon today?_____

3. What is the population of Ohio today?_____

4. Which state on the table has less than a million people living there?

   _____

5. Look at the names of the states. How are they arranged?

   _____

Apply to the Test

1. The first state admitted to the Union in the 1800s was

   ○ **A.** Louisiana

   ○ **B.** Ohio

   ○ **C.** New York

2. Ohio is more heavily populated than all of the following states EXCEPT

   ○ **A.** Pennsylvania

   ○ **B.** Indiana

   ○ **C.** Oregon

A graph is another device that helps you picture information. One special type of graph is a bar graph. It shows the relationship of information, called data, in the form of bars.

The graph below compares the population of ten states. The states are represented by bars. To find the population, first look at the height of the bar. Then match the height with the population numbers along the left side of the graph.

Activity

Directions Read the graph below. Then answer the questions.

Where Are People Living Now?

Population estimates from US Census Bureau, 7-1-99.

POPULATION

8,000,000	
7,000,000	
6,000,000	Missouri
5,000,000	
4,000,000	Kentucky
3,000,000	Oregon
2,000,000	
1,000,000	Delaware Wyoming
0	

Alabama   Georgia   Massachusetts   Nevada   Tennessee

STATES

180 Reading Nonfiction   Copying is Illegal.   Measuring Up to the OH Learning Outcomes • Reading

Lesson 7   Use Graphs

Skill Builder

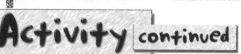

Activity continued

1. What are the names of the states being compared? _____
   _____

2. Which state on this graph has the most people living there?
   _____

3. Which state has the fewest people living there? _____

4. About how many people are living now in Oregon? _____

5. About how many people are living now in Kentucky? _____

B. Directions   In the space below, create a bar graph. Find out how many students are in each grade at your school. Represent this information in the form of a bar graph.

Go on to the next page ➤

**Apply to
the Test**

1. The population of Georgia is
   - ◯ **A.** over 8,000,000
   - ◯ **B.** over 7,000,000
   - ◯ **C.** over 6,000,000

2. Massachusetts is more heavily populated than all of the following states EXCEPT
   - ◯ **A.** Georgia
   - ◯ **B.** Alabama
   - ◯ **C.** Wyoming

When you retell something, you put it in your own words. Doing this helps you to better understand the information.

A. Directions Here is a paragraph from . . . If You Traveled West in a Covered Wagon. Retell it. On the lines below, put the information in the paragraph in your own words.

Back then nobody knew if the Oregon Territory was going to be part of America or if it was going to be part of England. Both countries had built forts in the territory. At the forts, trappers and Indians sold animal furs and skins, such as beaver, marten, and muskrat, and bought tools and supplies.

_____

_____

_____

_____

_____

_____

_____

_____

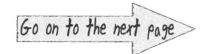

Go on to the next page

Activity continued

B. Directions Here is another paragraph from *. . . If You Traveled West in a Covered Wagon*. Retell it. On the lines below, put the information in the paragraph in your own words.

A covered wagon was a wagon with a white rounded top made of cloth. The cloth was called canvas and was rubbed with oil to make it waterproof. It was stretched over big wooden hoops that were bent from one side of the wagon to the other.

_____

_____

_____

_____

_____

_____

_____

Measuring Up to the OH Learning Outcomes • Reading

Activity continued

C. Directions   Here is another paragraph from
. . . *If You Traveled West in a Covered Wagon.* Retell it.
On the lines below, put the information in the
paragraph in your own words.

Inside the wagon there were hooks on the wooden hoops. On them you could hang milk cans, guns, bonnets, spoons, dolls, jackets, and anything else there was room for. Underneath the wagon between the back wheels there was a hook with a bucket of grease hanging down from it. The grease was rubbed on the wheels so that they would turn smoothly.

_____

_____

_____

_____

_____

_____

_____

What do you do when you read a word you do not know? One strategy is to use context clues. These context clues are found in the other words surrounding the unknown word.

Look at the sentences below.

> People told *incredible* stories about Oregon. They made it seem bigger than life. They made it sound like a magical place where flowers bloomed all year round.

You may not know the meaning of the word incredible. However, the rest of the sentences contain clues—bigger than life, magical, flowers blooming all year round. These clues help you see that incredible means "unbelievable, too good to be true."

 **Activity**

Directions Now try it on your own. In the sentences below, use context clues to figure out the meaning of each *italicized* word. Write your definition on the line after each sentence.

1. The label said that the blanket was *flammable*. Luis knew that he had to keep something that could catch fire away from the baby.

   _____

   _____

2. The bike needs oil. The gears are squeaking. You should *lubricate* them so that they work smoothly.

   _____

   _____

3. He felt nervous and afraid. He had serious *qualms* about going on the roller coaster.

   _____

   _____

 Measuring Up to the OH Learning Outcomes • Reading

Activity continued

4. The video showed how the earth began to *quake*.
As the earth shook and trembled, the house began to fall.

_____

_____

5. The king was losing his *domination* over the colonies. The more
the colonists spoke up, the more control he lost.

_____

_____

6. When we visited Hawaii, we saw a *dormant* volcano. It had not
shown any signs of action for hundreds of years.

_____

_____

7. The pirate knew the mate would *double-cross* him. He waited for
the moment the mate would show he was not loyal.

_____

_____

8. They searched for *fossils* along the riverbank. They found several
rocks that showed traces of animals and plants from ages ago.

_____

_____

9. The nurse tried to improve *sanitary* conditions. Keeping the homes
clean and free of germs was his goal.

_____

_____

10. "The price is *outrageous*!" Amanda said. "I can go next store and
buy the same thing for half as much."

_____

_____

Directions: Read the selection and answer the questions.

> This article discusses a new theory about tickling. Read the article to find out what it is.

Tickle Theory
Rosalind Reid

Sneak up on your little brother and tickle him. If he's ticklish, he'll laugh, of course. But Christine Harris wonders why he laughs. "It's actually quite bizarre," she says, "that someone rubbing their fingers up and down your sides or foot makes you laugh."

Harris is a psychologist at the University of California-San Diego, whose cousins used to tickle her as a kid. It was more torture than fun, but she laughed anyway. As a scientist, she now wants to understand the experience. She has looked at whether ticklish laughter and humorous laughter–the kind you experience when you hear a funny joke–are the same. (They aren't.) She has even rigged up a tickle machine to study whether people laugh more when they know they're being tickled by an actual person. (They don't.)

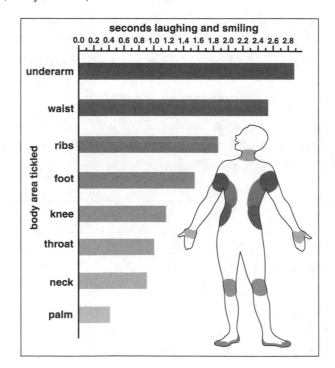

In one of her experiments, Harris mapped people's tickle zones. She asked some students to tickle other students in various places, then measured how long the subjects laughed and smiled during tickling sessions. The biggest response—an average of more than 2.6 seconds of laughing and smiling came when students were tickled under their arms. The other top ticklish spots were the waist and the ribs.

Tickle zones aren't in the most sensitive places on the body, like the mouth and fingers. Instead, they're parts of the body that we automatically protect. (When you're tickled on the torso, for example, you pull your arms tight to defend yourself.) These protective reflexes might have helped early humans survive, which might explain why tickling developed.

At any rate, that explanation makes a great excuse. The next time you tickle your little brother, tell him you're only doing it for his own good. After all, you're not tickling him to turn him into a red, gasping heap. Of course not. The real reason for tickling him is to hone his survival skills.

Go On

1. Christine Harris's tickle theory is that tickling

   ○ **A.** is a way of making them happier.

   ○ **B.** may have helped early people hone their survival skills.

   ○ **C.** is one of the most annoying things to do.

2. In Harris's experiment, she studied tickle zones by measuring

   ○ **A.** how long people laughed and smiled.

   ○ **B.** the amount of times people flinched.

   ○ **C.** blood pressure and heart beat.

3. According to the article, the most ticklish area is

   ○ **A.** under the arms.

   ○ **B.** the neck.

   ○ **C.** the ribs.

4. Tickle zones can be found

   ○ **A.** In the most sensitive parts of the body.

   ○ **B.** Anywhere on the body.

   ○ **C.** In parts of the body that we protect.

5. Using the chart, indicate how many seconds people laughed and smiled when they were tickled on their knee?

   ○ **A.** 1.8 seconds

   ○ **B.** 1.1 seconds

   ○ **C.** 2.0 seconds

How to Write a Short Response

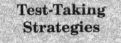

What's Expected on the Test?

You have already learned how to answer multiple-choice questions for the Ohio Proficiency Test. Now you will learn how to write a short response to a question based on a selection you have read.

When you answer the short response question, you will put your ideas into writing. Instead of choosing an answer like you did when you answered a mulitple-choice question, you will write a sentence or two to answer a question. You can look back at the selection at any time you if you need to.

Test-Taking Strategies

Read the Question Carefully

Make sure that you read the question carefully and that you understand it. If you misread the question, your response will be incorrect.

Go Back and Reread

If you need to find the answer to the question, go back to the selection and reread. Even if you don't feel that you need to reread, do it anyway. This way you'll make sure that the details and facts you are writing are correct.

Organize Your Thoughts

Think about what you want to write before you write. Ask yourself: What do I want to say first? What details should I include? Did I fully answer the question? Organize your ideas first so that your answer is clear and so that you don't leave out, or repeat information.

Be Accurate

The facts and details you include in your response must be accurate. Check to see that you didn't misspell a name or place. Make sure you don't confuse the names of people, places, or things.

Use Only the Space Provided

The space you are given to write your response is a good indication of how long your answer should be. If you only use one or two lines, you probably didn't answer the question fully. If your response takes up more space than you are given, you might be including unnecessary details and information.

Go on to the next page

Lesson 11

How to Write a Short Response

Directions Use the questions in the right-hand column to guide your reading.

Teddy's Bear
—Janeen R. Adil

Theodore "Teddy" Roosevelt, America's twenty-sixth president, was famous for accomplishing many important things while he was in office. Something he **1** didn't do, however, made him just as famous. And because of it, one of the best-loved toys ever created **2** was named after him.

In November 1902, President Roosevelt traveled south to settle a boundary dispute between Mississippi and Louisiana. While he was there, he took some time off to go bear hunting. Several reporters and a well-known newspaper artist named Clifford Berryman joined the president's hunting trip.

The hunters didn't have much luck. Finally, on the last day of the hunt, the president spotted a bear. As he carefully aimed his rifle, the animal turned around. It was only a cub! Teddy Roosevelt loved to hunt, but **3** he refused to shoot the frightened little bear.

Clifford Berryman thought this was a wonderful opportunity for a drawing. He sketched a cartoon of President Roosevelt turning his back on the cub, unwilling to shoot the small creature. Soon Berryman's black-and-white drawing was appearing in newspapers all over the country. People everywhere liked the cartoon and thought it showed the president **4** to be a kind-hearted man.

One of those who saw and enjoyed the drawing was Morris Michtom, a candy store owner in Brooklyn, New York. He and his wife, Rose, knew how to make stuffed toys, and the cartoon gave them an idea. The Michtoms found some brown plush fabric and cut out pieces for a bear with movable arms and legs. Then **5** they sewed the bear and added buttons for its eyes.

1 Make a prediction about what would make Teddy Roosevelt famous.

2 The **main idea** of this selection is stated in the first paragraph. What is the main idea?

3 Retell what happened to Teddy Roosevelt on his bear hunting trip.

4 Why did people like the cartoon of the president?

5 Summarize what you have learned about the Michtoms

READING GUIDE

The Michtoms placed the new toy bear, a copy of Berryman's cartoon, and a sign that read "Teddy's Bear" in the front window of their store. The bears sold quickly, and so did the next few that the Michtoms made. When Morris saw how popular the bear were, he knew he would need the president's **6** permission to continue using his name.

Morris wrote a letter to the White House and received a handwritten reply from Theodore Roosevelt himself. "I don't think my name is likely to be worth much in the bear business," the president wrote, "but you are welcome to use it." So the Michtoms went to work, making one teddy bear after another.

Since Rose and Morris made the bears themselves and still had a candy store to manage, they produced the bears slowly at first. Eventually they closed the **7** candy store, and the Michtom family business became the Ideal Toy Company, one of America's biggest toy makers. Soon other companies in the United States **8** and Europe were producing bears of all shapes, sizes, and prices. Some of the most beautiful stuffed bears were made in Germany by Margarete Steiff and her workers.

In just a few years, teddy bears had become extremely popular. Other items related to the stuffed bears were sold too. Not only could one buy clothing for a teddy bear, but there were also bear puzzles, bear books, bear games, bear banks—all sorts of toys and amusements! Teddy bears had become as important to children as blocks, dolls, and balls had been for **9** generations.

Today teddy bears remain a favorite of boys and girls everywhere. Many adults love to collect and display them, too. Hundreds of millions of teddy bears have been produced since Teddy Roosevelt's hunting trip so many years ago. Who could have guessed that the story of an unlucky president and a frightened bear cub would have such a happy ending?

GUIDED QUESTIONS

6 Use the information you're told to **make inferences**. Why would Morris need the president's permission to continue using the president's name?

7 **Make inferences.** Why did the Michtoms close the candy store?

8 **Make inferences.** Why did other companies begin making bears?

9 Was is the **main idea** of this paragraph? Which **details** support the main idea?

Go on to the next page →

How to Write a Short Response

READING GUIDE

Sample Short-Response Question

1. Was Teddy Roosevelt's prediction correct about his name never being worth much in the bear business? Explain your answer.

10

_____

_____

_____

_____

GUIDED QUESTIONS

10 Your answer to this question will be based on information from the article.

Directions Write your answer to the short-response question on the lines provided above.

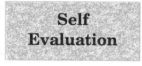 **Self Evaluation**

Ask yourself
● Did I answer the question
● Did I explain my answer?
● Is my answer clear and easy to read?
● Are the details I included correct?

How Your Response Will Be Evaluated

Your response will be evaluated by teachers. The teachers use a rubric to score your answer. The rubric lets you and your teachers know what an excellent, satisfactory, and unsatisfactory response contains.

Your response will be scored on a scale of 0-2. A 2 is the best score you can receive. It means that you answered the question clearly and correctly. Aim to receive a score of 2.

Short-Answer Rubric

2	• Is complete and appropriate • Demonstrates a thorough understanding of the reading selection • Indicates logical reasoning and conclusions • Is accurate, relevant, comprehensive, and detailed
1	• Is partially appropriate • Contains minor flaws in reasoning or neglects to address some aspect of the item or question • Is mostly accurate and relevant but lacks comprehensiveness • Demonstrates an incomplete understanding of the reading selection or demonstrates an inability to make coherent meaning from the text
0	• Shows no understanding of the item or the student fails to respond to the item

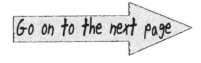

Go on to the next page

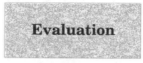
Sample Response

Teddy Roosevelt's prediction is not correct. He predicts that his name won't be worth much in the bear business. Teddy bears, however, quickly became popular and are still a beloved toy for children and adults.

Evaluation

This response would receive a score of 2. It states that the prediction is incorrect. It then explains why it is incorrect using details from the selection. The response is also accurate, clear, and easy to read.

Directions Look again at your own answer. Using the rubric, write an evaluation of your response. Use the lines below to write your evaluation.

_____

_____

_____

_____

_____

 Measuring Up to the OH Learning Outcomes • Reading

The **main idea** is the most important point that the author makes. Supporting **details** are words or phrases that tell about the main idea.

An article generally has one overall main idea. This is the main point of the article. You will also find that each paragraph has a main idea. Often, but not always, the main idea will be stated in the topic sentence of the paragraph. Read this passage from a school newspaper article. The chart identifies the main idea and supporting details.

> The fourth grade held its annual food festival this week. Each student brought an ethnic food of his or her choice. Students participated in an exciting cultural experience as they tasted delicious appetizers, main dishes, and desserts. The festival featured cuisine from countries such as Mexico, India, Turkey, Russia, Zimbabwe, and Japan.

Main Idea: Fourth graders had their annual food festival.

Supporting Detail	Supporting Detail	Supporting Detail
Each student brought a dish.	Students tasted appetizers, main dishes, and desserts.	There was cuisine from many foreign countries.

Go on to the next page ➡

Lesson 13 — Discern Main Idea and Supporting Details

Skill Builder

Directions As you read the article below, look for the main idea and notice the supporting details. Then answer the questions.

How Wild Flowers Get Their Names
—*Jennifer Ewing*

Have you ever seen a lady's slipper or a shooting star? These are not your mother's shoe or a bright light in the dark sky. These are names of wild flowers. The petals of the shooting star blast out in every direction from the center of the flower, and a lady's slipper looks as though it could fit on a very small foot. There's a lot of imagination used in naming wild flowers.

Only in a field of wild flowers might you find a *cluster*[1] of blue witches next to a row of Chinese houses. What do you think baby blue eyes or pussy paws look like? Little elephant-heads have flowers that look like two big ears and the trunk of an elephant. If you use your imagination, you can see the eyes and beak of an owl in the flower of the owl's clover. If you pinch the toadflax flower, the frog mouth opens. These wild flowers are all names for the way they look.

Some wildflowers got their names because of the way they were used. Coyote tobacco was smoked and chewed (but not by coyotes). You can eat some wild flowers.[2] Miners lettuce was eaten by miners (and American Indians). Wild strawberries might taste good on shortcake. Cow parsnip is a tasty herb for cattle.

The story of how the forget-me-not got its name is a sad story about love. Two lovers were walking along the Danube, a river in Germany. The girl saw some beautiful blue flowers growing along the bank. She asked her sweetheart to pick them for her. They were growing on a very steep bank, which was dangerous to climb. He didn't want to disappoint her and climbed the bank to pick them for her. He lost his balance and fell into the river. As he feel, he threw the flowers up onto the bank. As he was sinking under the water, he called out, "Forget me not."

---

[1]**cluster:** group

[2]Not all wild flowers can be eaten safely. Do not eat wildflowers on your own. Never eat a wildflower without getting an expert's advice.

Activity continued

These kinds of names make it easier to identify and remember some of the many types of wild flowers. Wild flowers often have different nicknames in different parts of the United States. If you have wild flowers around your house, try to come up with your own names for them. Use your imagination.

1. Does the title of this selection tell the main idea of the selection? Explain why or why not.

_____

_____

2. What is the main idea of the second paragraph?

_____

_____

3. What is one supporting detail for this main idea?

_____

_____

4. Look at the third paragraph. What is the topic sentence of this paragraph?

_____

_____

5. How would you summarize the main idea of the third paragraph in your own words?

_____

_____

Go on to the next page ➡

Activity continued

6. What are two supporting details for the main idea of the third paragraph?

_____

_____

7. What is the main idea of the fourth paragraph?

_____

_____

Apply to the Test

1. Which of the following is not a supporting detail about how wildflowers have gotten their names?

◯ **A.** based on how they look

◯ **B.** from foods they taste like

◯ **C.** for the way they're used

2. Which sentence in the second paragraph tells the main idea of this paragraph?

◯ **A.** the first sentence

◯ **B.** the second sentence

◯ **C.** the last sentence

3. In your opinion, which wildflower from the selection has the most interesting name? Explain how the flower got its name and why you think the name is interesting.

_____

_____

_____

_____

Compare and Contrast

When you **compare** things, you think about how they are alike. When you **contrast** things, you think about how they are different. When you compare and contrast, look for similarities and differences.

Graphic devices such as charts and Venn diagrams can help you compare and contrast two subjects. For instance, look at this Venn diagram to compare and contrast *apples* and *oranges*.

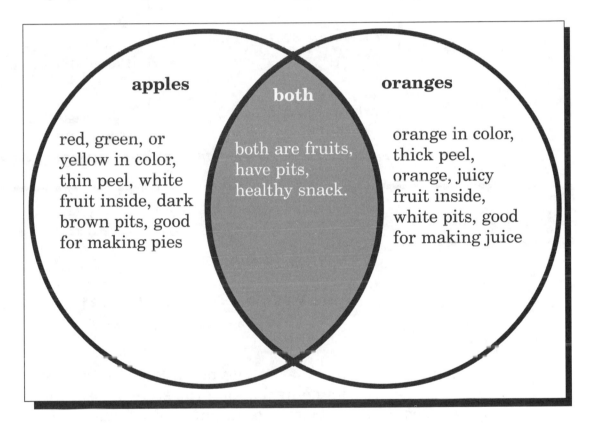

apples

red, green, or yellow in color, thin peel, white fruit inside, dark brown pits, good for making pies

both

both are fruits, have pits, healthy snack.

oranges

orange in color, thick peel, orange, juicy fruit inside, white pits, good for making juice

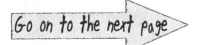

Go on to the next page

You can also compare and contrast two subjects with a simple chart. Look at this chart which compares two sisters named Lisa and Rachel.

Comparisons	Contrasts
Both have red hair.	Lisa has freckles, Rachel does not.
Both enjoy swimming.	Lisa likes to play soccer. Rachel likes to play softball.
Both are good readers.	Rachel is outgoing. Lisa is shy.

Directions Read the following passage about wildflowers. Then use the Venn diagram to compare and contrast daisies and black-eyed susans.

How Wild Flowers Get Their Names
—Jennifer Ewing

Along with many other species of wildflowers, daisies and black-eyed susans are commonly found in the state of Delaware. These two types of wildflowers belong to the sunflower family. The daisy is a member of the white wildflower group while the black-eyed susan is categorized as a yellow wildflower.

The flower of a daisy has a large, somewhat flat yellow center that is surrounded by white petals. The petals are close together and overlap. Black-eyed susans, on the other hand, have an upraised brown center that looks like a gumdrop. The petals are yellow and they are longer than the petals of the daisy. Black-eyed susans, however, have fewer petals than daisies do and there is space between the petals.

202 Reading Nonfiction   Copying is Illegal.   Measuring Up to the OH Learning Outcomes • Reading

Activity continued

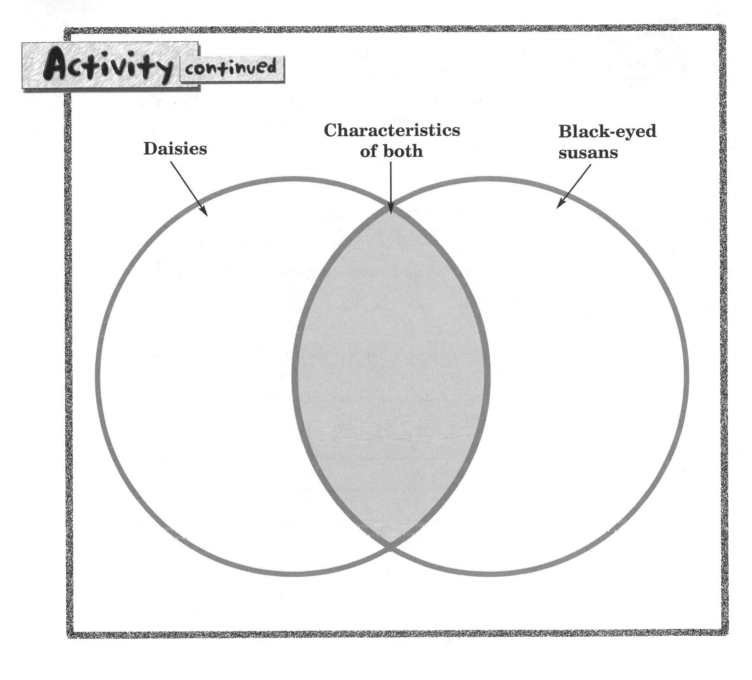

Daisies

Characteristics of both

Black-eyed susans

Go on to the next page

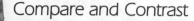

Apply to the Test

1. Which of the following is a comparison about wildflowers?

   ○ **A.** Blue witches and Chinese houses are named for the way they look.

   ○ **B.** Some flowers are named for the way they look and others are named for how they're used.

   ○ **C.** The forget-me-not is a sad story and an interesting story.

2. Which statement makes a contrast?

   ○ **A.** Blue eyes and pussy paws look like their names.

   ○ **B.** Cow parsnip is eaten and coyote tobacco is chewed.

   ○ **C.** Wildflowers have different nicknames.

3. Compare and contrast the way that wildflowers are named. What is one similarity about how many wildflowers get their names? What is one difference about how wildflowers are named?

   _____

   _____

   _____

An **effect** is something that happens. A **cause** is the reason why it happened. To find out the effect, ask yourself the question, What happened? To find out the cause, ask yourself Why did it happen?

Understanding cause and effect will help you see how important events fit together. Keep in mind that a cause may often have more than one effect. For instance, a blizzard (the cause) can create dangerous road conditions (an effect) and an electrical blackout (an effect).

Look for signal words as you read that can help you identify cause and effect. Here are some examples of signal words: *because*, *therefore*, *as a result*, *why*, and *for this reason*.

Here is another example of cause and effect. Imagine that you are at the beach. You forgot to put on lotion and you notice that your shoulders burn. The sun is the cause of your sunburn. The effect of the sunburn is painful skin.

Directions Read the following selection. Then answer the questions that follow it.

Flicking Tongues
—*Jack Myers*

Why do snakes flick their tongues? People have been curious about that question for thousands of years. Many different answers have been suggested. But only recently have scientists learned enough about snakes to get close to an answer.

To people who don't like snakes, the flicking tongue might seem evil. Some people might think it carries poison, but it's easy to show that idea is wrong. Poisonous snakes deliver their venom with special fangs. Most other snakes, even little garter snakes, do a lot of tongue flicking. But none of them has venom on its tongue.

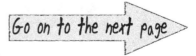

Go on to the next page

Activity continued

From the way a snake uses its tongue, it seems to be tasting. Taste and smell are two senses that are nice to have, even though you and I don't depend on them very much. We depend more on sight and hearing. But if you lived down among grasses and rocks as a snake does, taste and smell might give you a lot of information about your part of the world.

A Senseless Tongue?

The taste idea looked sensible. But at first, a study of snake tongues showed some problems. Scientists discovered that a snake's tongue doesn't have any taste buds, the little gadgets packed with nerve endings that give you your sense of taste. Snake tongues also lack nerves that could send messages to their brains.

The scientists tried again. They studied the snake's head. It has two cavities[1], one opening to the mouth and one to the nose. At the back of the nose cavity there is a patch of cells with nerve connections to the brain. That's where the snake does its smelling.

A different bundle of nerves goes to two little hollow structures within the roof of the mouth. Each has a little hole to the mouth cavity below. These have come to be called the vomeronasal organs. That's where the snake does its tasting.

In one experiment, some soot (finely powdered carbon) was spread on the ground where a snake was flicking its tongue. Later, the carbon particles were found in the vomeronasal organs. Of course that left the question of how the carbon particles got there.

---

[1]**cavities:** a hole or hollow space in something

Activity continued

It was natural to suppose that a snake might taste by slipping the two tips of its tongue into the little holes of the vomeronasal organs. But high-speed movies told a different story. When the tongue flicks out, its two tips are pulled apart before they touch anything. As the tongue is pulled in, the two tips are dragged across little pads on the bottom of the mouth. And then when the snake closes its mouth, those two pads rise up to touch the openings to the vomeronasal organs.

There's a lot we still do not know about the everyday life of a snake. But one of its features is no longer a mystery. By flicking its tongue, the snake brings back to its vomeronasal organs whatever chemicals are out there. The snake is always tasting its environment.

Why a Forked Tongue?

One special use of the snake's tongue is to help it follow the trail of its prey. Scientists have watched carefully to figure out how snakes do it. It's easy to watch garter snakes, which prey on earthworms. For garter snakes, a good trail can be made with the slime of earthworms. And the trail can be made through a maze of pathways.

Here's the idea we have about why a snake is so good at following a taste trail. It is always pulling back tasty chemicals on the two forks of its tongue. And nerve connections from the vomeronasal organs are always comparing the amount of taste brought in by the right and left fork. Equal amounts of taste on the right and left mean the trail goes straight. More taste on one side means the trail must be turning toward that side. You can say that the snake's forked tongue gives it stereoscopic[2] taste.

[2]**stereoscopic:** able to see two different points of view

Go on to the next page

Skill Builder

Activity continued

1. Scientists discovered that snakes don't have taste buds.
   What effect did this have on their research?

   _____

   _____

2. Consider where a snake lives and how it moves.
   What causes a snake to need a good sense of taste of smell?

   _____

   _____

3. What question did scientists have when they discovered soot
   in the vomersonasal organs?

   _____

   _____

4. When happens when a snake flicks out its tongue?

   _____

   _____

5. As a snake follows its prey, it flicks its forked tongue.
   What effect will more taste on one side of the forked tongue
   have on the snake's movement?

   _____

   _____

   _____

Apply to the Test

1. What caused people to be curious about snakes for thousands of years?

   ○ **A.** why they carried poison

   ○ **B.** why they flicked their tongue

   ○ **C.** why they followed their prey

2. What will cause a snake to continue straight on a taste trail?

   ○ **A.** more taste on the right side of the forked tongue

   ○ **B.** the absence of taste on both sides of the forked tongue

   ○ **C.** equal amounts of taste on the right and left side of the forked tongue

3. What did the scientists learn about the snake's tongue from high-speed movies?

   _____

   _____

   _____

   _____

   _____

Can you tell the difference between a fact and an opinion? A **fact** is a statement that is true and that can be proven to be correct. An **opinion** is a statement that tells what a person believes or thinks.

Sometimes writers state an opinion as if it were fact. Being aware of the difference between a fact and an opinion will help you evaluate information.

Notice the statements of fact versus the statements of opinion in the chart below.

Fact	Opinion
California is a state.	California is the prettiest state.
California has popular tourist attractions.	California is a better place for a vacation than New York.

 **Directions** Read "Tongue Feats" and answer the questions below.

Tongue Feats

—*Suzanne Emler*

Does your tongue hang low?
Does it wobble to and fro?
Can you tie it in a knot?
Can you tie it in a bow?

This new version of an old camp song may sound silly to you, but some animals could answer "yes" to all four questions!

Activity continued

The chameleon's tongue, for example, is not just long enough to tie in a bow—it could wrap an entire package. Chameleons aren't very interested in giftwrap, of course, but long tongues are also useful for catching food. First, the lizard creeps to an unsuspecting insect. It points its head, opens its mouth, and zing! Its tongue shoots from the back of its mouth like a harpoon. When it pulls its tongue back, the sticky, clublike tip holds lunch. Inside the chameleon's mouth, the tongue bunches up like an accordion to wait for dessert.

Frogs use their tongues to catch insects, too. A frog's tongue is shorter than a chameleon's, but it's stretchy and strong. It's attached at the front of the mouth instead of the back. The frog flips it forward like an elastic whip when a tasty insect flies nearby. A sticky coating helps trap the insect. When not zapping snacks, the frog's tongue is folded neatly inside its mouth.

The longest, stickiest tongue belongs to the anteater. One drop of anteater saliva could be stretched into a gummy string about a foot long. The anteater pokes its tongue into ant and termite tunnels and scoops out its meals. Then **barbed**[1] spikes on the tongue grind against spikes on the roof of the mouth to crush the ants before they are swallowed.

The woodpecker uses its long tongue to explore insect nests. First, the bird drills a hole in tree bark with its hard beak. Then the tongue scrapes bugs from their hiding places. Some woodpeckers' tongues have a barbed tip for spearing insects. A woodpecker's tongue is attached to a set of delicate bones and stretchy tissue that curves under the jaw, around the head, and into the right nostril.

---

[1]**barbed:** has spikes on it

Go on to the next page

Activity continued

The archerfish's tongue is neither long nor sticky, but it's still useful for catching dinner. The fish tilts its body upward and floats near the water's surface. Then it curls its tongue against the roof of its mouth and shoots a stream of water at an insect on a nearby leaf. When the insect falls into the water, it's gobbled up by the waiting fish. People who study this fish have discovered that it also squirts at things it can't eat—like blinking eyes.

Unlike most other animals, snakes have no taste buds on their tongues and cannot use them as weapons. Have you ever seen a snake flickering its tongue? It's collecting **molecules**[2] from the air. Back inside its mouth, the tongue passes over a special organ that reads the smells and tastes of those molecules. The tongue's forked shape helps it gather as many molecules as possible. The creepy flickering also scares away predators.

Now that you know how terrific tongues can be, don't be tongue-tied: give three cheers for tongue feats!

---

[2]**molecules:** very small particles

1. Does this article mostly have statements of fact or statements of opinion? Explain your answer.

   _____

   _____

   _____

2. What part of the following statement is an opinion?
   The creepy flickering also scares away predators.

   _____

   _____

   _____

212 Reading Nonfiction   Copying is Illegal.   Measuring Up to the OH Learning Outcomes • Reading

Activity continued

3. What makes it an opinion?

_____

_____

_____

4. Is the following statement a fact or an opinion? Explain why.

A frog's tongue is shorter than a chameleon's, but it's stretchy and strong.

_____

_____

_____

5. The last statement of this selection contains an opinion. What is it? What makes it an opinion?

_____

_____

_____

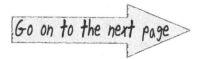
Go on to the next page

Apply to the Test

1. Which statement is an opinion?

   ○ **A.** Chameleons aren't very interested in giftwrap.

   ○ **B.** Frogs use their tongues to catch insects.

   ○ **C.** The anteater pokes its tongue into ant and termite tunnels.

2. Which of the following statements is **not** a fact?

   ○ **A.** Unlike most other animals, snakes have no taste buds on their tongues.

   ○ **B.** A sticky coating helps trap the insect.

   ○ **C.** This new version of an old camp song may sound silly to you.

3. The selections states that, *"The longest stickiest tongue belongs to the anteater."* This statement seems like an opinion, but it is a fact. Explain how you would prove it to be a fact.

   _____

   _____

   _____

   _____

   _____

214 Reading Nonfiction   Copying is Illegal.   Measuring Up to the OH Learning Outcomes • Reading

An **inference** is an educated guess that you make based on the information you know. You naturally make inferences as you read because authors don't explain everything. They expect you to "read between the lines" and to know certain things. In other words, you figure out what is going on by filling in information that the author doesn't directly tell you.

An author usually gives you enough details to make the assumptions or inferences that are necessary to understand the text. For example, read the following passage.

> Julio wiped the sweat from his forehead. There was not a cloud in the sky and the blazing sun beat down on him. It seemed that Julio was constantly putting his canteen to his lips to quench his thirst.

Did you realize from the details in this passage that it was a hot day? If you did, you made an inference. The passage never states that it was hot. The details, however, help you infer the temperature.

Directions Read "Blimping Up" and make inferences based on each passage from the selection.

Blimping Up
—Carolee Brockmann

Why would a normal 8-year-old girl from the New Jersey suburbs want to be a blimp pilot? Something about floating in the sky and something about balloons drew Laura Sheft to this unusual career at an early age.

"I HAD WONDERFUL DREAMS at night about flying in balloons. Balloons that I could steer!" Laura says. "I didn't know what they were called then, but I was dreaming about blimps." At age 14, Laura Sheft became the youngest balloon pilot in the country, and at 23 she got her first job driving a blimp. Today, Laura is the president of Airship Images, a Saddle River, New Jersey,

Go on to the next page

Activity continued

company that provides all types of flying machines, including blimps, to its customers.

Laura's parents helped Laura turn her nighttime fantasy into a daytime goal. "I don't think I would have done it without their encouragement and support," she says. "One of my earliest memories is my father taking me to the dictionary and crossing out the word `can't."

When she was 8, Laura asked her father if she could have balloon lessons. "I don't think he quite heard her right," says Laura's mom, Teresa Sheft. "But he said yes, and when Laura turned 13, she held him to his promise."

Laura found out about a balloon convention in Maryland. The family packed up for a weekend **excursion**[1]. Laura's parents hoped that one trip in a hot air balloon would satisfy her desire for floating, and then she would find a safer hobby, a little closer to home—and the ground!

When the balloon landed after Laura's first ride, her mother was **dismayed**[2] to discover that Laura loved it. She was hooked. She realized that she had to learn how to pilot both hot air balloons and fixed wing planes before getting close to the huge and very expensive steerable blimps. Impressed by her determination, her parents swallowed their worries and helped her find lessons. "I am so lucky to have had parents who believed in me and took me seriously," says Laura. "At first, I think they were hoping I would grow out of it, but they never laughed at me or told me to think about something else."

---

[1]**excursion:** a short trip

[2]**dismayed:** upset and worried about something

Activity continued

Laura made her first solo hot air balloon flight at age 14. Her family always took her seriously, but not all adults did. Her high school guidance counselor said she was crazy and wondered what she would ever do with balloon training. Since then, she has ballooned across the English Channel, over the Swiss Alps, and across the Sierra Nevada mountains; she has provided TV camera coverage over Super Bowls, baseball championships, and tennis championships; she has observed marine mammal populations from the air with Sea World scientists; and she has managed a successful airship company. Laura Sheft has plenty of ideas of what to do with balloon training! And she knows what it feels like to make dreams come true. She says, "It's wonderful to do what you've always wanted to do! I've wanted to pilot a blimp ever since I was a little girl. And here I am."

Laura's parents helped Laura turn her nighttime fantasy into a daytime goal. "I don't think I would have done it without their encouragement and support," she says. "One of my earliest memories is my father taking me to the dictionary and crossing out the word can't."

1. What can you infer about Laura's father from the dictionary episode?

_____

_____

_____

Go on to the next page

Activity continued

2. What detail helped you make this inference?

_____

_____

When she was 8, Laura asked her father if she could have balloon lessons. "I don't think he quite heard her right," says Laura's mom, Teresa Sheft. "But he said yes, and when Laura turned 13, she held him to his promise."

3. How do you think Laura's father felt about giving her balloon lessons?

_____

_____

4. Why do you think that Laura had to wait until she was thirteen years old to begin ballooning lessons?

_____

_____

_____

5. What can you infer about the guidance counselor's view of balloon training?

_____

_____

1. Laura turned her dreams into a reality because she was

   ○ **A.** crazy

   ○ **B.** intelligent

   ○ **C.** determined

2. Why did Laura's parents hope that one balloon trip would satisfy her?

   ○ **A.** They were worried about their daughter's safety.

   ○ **B.** They were worried about how much lessons would cost.

   ○ **C.** They were afraid of heights.

3. What advice would Laura give to kids about pursuing their dreams? Use at least one detail from the selection to support your answer.

   _____

   _____

   _____

   _____

   _____

Some words can be used as nouns and verbs. Depending on the context of the word in a sentence, you can usually figure out if the word is a person, place, or thing, or an action. For instance, in the title of the article, "Blimping Up," blimping is a verb. As a noun, the word *blimp* means *an airship shaped like a balloon.*

Activity

Directions   Read each sentence below which is from the article, "Blimping Up." The bold word is a word that can function as both a noun and a verb. Then answer the questions.

*Balloons that I could **steer**!*

1. Is *steer* used as a noun or a verb? _____

2. What does *steer* mean when it's used as a noun? _____

3. What does *steer* mean when it's used as a verb? _____

*Laura's parents helped Laura **turn** her nighttime fantasy into a daytime goal.*

4. Is *turn* used as a noun or a verb? _____

5. What does *turn* mean when it's used as a noun? _____

6. What does *turn* mean when it's used as a verb?

_____

*I've wanted to **pilot** a blimp ever since I was a little girl.*

7. Is *pilot* used as a noun or a verb? _____

8. What does *pilot* mean when it's used as a noun? _____

9. What does *pilot* mean when it's used as a verb? _____

*"I don't think I would have done it without their encouragement and **support**."*

10. How is the word *support* used in this sentence? _____

Apply to the Test

1. Which word is both a noun and a verb?

  ○ **A.** believe

  ○ **B.** desire

  ○ **C.** night

2. The word *crossing* can be used as

  ○ **A.** only a noun

  ○ **B.** only a verb

  ○ **C.** a noun and a verb

3. You won't find the words *blimping* or *ballooning* in the dictionary. Why do you think the author turned the nouns *blimp* and *balloon* into these verbs? What suffix did she add to change the words from nouns to verbs?

  _____

  _____

  _____

  _____

  _____

Directions: Read the selection and answer the questions.

A Dad Who Has Babies

Marilyn Singer

The seahorse lives in the sea, but it isn't a horse. It's a fish—an unusual one. Most fish swim on their bellies with their heads in front and their tails behind. But the seahorse swims upright: with its head up and its long, curvy tail down. Most fish are covered with small, shiny scales. But not the seahorse. Its bumpy, bony skeleton is covered with tough, bare skin.

Perhaps the strangest thing about seahorses is the way they have their babies. It's the father seahorse, not the mother, who gives birth. A father seahorse has a pouch on his belly. The mother seahorse lays her eggs in this pouch. Inside the pouch, the babies get food and oxygen. They grow bigger every day. The mother seahorse spends her whole life with the father seahorse. She greets the father every morning. She swims and dances in the water with him. But she does not take care of the babies at all. That's the father's job.

When the baby seahorses are ready to be born, the father grasps a seaweed stem, a piece of coral, a sponge, or another object with his tail. He bends back and forth. Soon his pouch opens, and out pops a baby seahorse. The tiny baby looks just like its parents. It can already swim and feed itself. The rest of the babies are born in the next few days. They swim away and never return to their father's pouch. After all the babies are born, the father gets to rest. But very soon the mother seahorse will put more eggs in his pouch, and he'll have more babies to take care of. In just a few months these babies will be ready to be seahorse mothers and fathers themselves.

1. What can you infer about seahorses based on the last line of this selection?

    ○ **A.** seahorses are fish not mammals

    ○ **B.** seahorses like to rest

    ○ **C.** seahorse babies grow up quickly

222 Reading Nonfiction   Copying is Illegal.   Measuring Up to the OH Learning Outcomes • Reading

2. What is the main idea of this selection?

○ **A.** seahorses can swim as soon as they're born

○ **B.** seahorses are unusual creatures

○ **C.** seahorses live in the water

3. Which statement belongs in a summary of this selection?

○ **A.** The father seahorse, not the mother, gives birth.

○ **B.** The babies grow bigger every day.

○ **C.** The father grasps a seaweed stem with his tail.

4. Which of the following is an opinion, not a fact, about seahorses?

○ **A.** Female seahorses don't take care of the babies.

○ **B.** Seahorses are strange and extremely peculiar.

○ **C.** The tiny baby looks just like its parents.

5. What causes the father's pouch to open?

○ **A.** the eggs burst out of the pouch when it becomes to full

○ **B.** the mother grabs the pouch with her tail and opens it

○ **C.** the father bends back and forth while grasping something with its tail

6. How are the roles of the father and mother seahorse unusual compared to other creatures?

_____

_____

_____

_____

How to Write an Extended Response

What's Expected on the Test?

The third type of question that you will answer on the Ohio Proficiency Test is the extended response question. An extended response is a long response. You will need to write an answer that thoroughly and clearly answers the question. The amount of space that you are given for your response is a good indication of how long your answer should be.

Sometimes the question will have more than one part. For instance, you may be asked to compare and contrast two things. Or, you may need to summarize information and give your opinion about it. Your answer to the extended response question will show how well you understood what you read.

These test-taking strategies will help you answer extended response questions.

Test-Taking Strategies

Read the Question Carefully

Make sure you read the question carefully and that you understand it. Notice if the question has more than one part. Pay attention to any special instructions. For instance, are you asked to give two examples or are you told to support your opinion with details?

Think About Your Answer First

Don't just start writing. Think about how you will respond first. If you think through your thoughts in your head, you can organize what you want to say.

Use the Best Examples

Support your answer with details from the selection. Choose the best examples to back up your answer. The examples and details that you choose will show your understanding of what you have read, as well as the question.

Be Accurate

When you read nonfiction selections, you will probably come across some unfamiliar terms or names of things, objects, and places. Make sure you the spell the terms and the names correctly. If you mention a date or the purpose of something, check to see that the information is accurate.

Proofread Your Response

Read your response after you finish writing it. See if your answer truly answers the question. Also look for sentences that are unclear or that don't make sense. Correct spelling, capitalization, and punctuation mistakes.

READING GUIDE

GUIDED QUESTIONS

Directions Put your reading strategies to work as you read "What Turkeys Eat for Thanksgiving." The questions will help you think about important aspects of the story and the extended response question.

What Turkeys Eat for Thanksgiving
—*Leslie Dendy*

1 MOST PEOPLE THINK of a turkey as a golden-brown bird that comes out of an oven. But let's think about turkeys having dinner instead of being dinner.

Long before any humans arrived in North America, millions of wild turkeys were strutting around in the woods. They're still here, in forests from coast to coast, although it may be hard to catch a glimpse of them. They can run as fast as horses and they can fly up to fifty-five miles per hour.

2 Wild turkeys are big birds with big appetites to match. They gobble, gobble almost everything in sight. They eat lots of ordinary bird food such as seeds, berries, and insects, but they don't stop there. They also gulp down frogs and lizards, salamanders and snakes, grapes and grass—and even crabs and cactus fruits.

3 They don't chew their food, because turkeys have no teeth. Like other birds, they swallow their meals in chunks, then wait for their gizzards to grind everything up. The gizzard is a tough, muscular sort of stomach with hard ridges inside. As the muscles squeeze tight, the ridges crush the food. There are usually stones inside, too, which the bird has swallowed to improve the grinding action. (You can see a gizzard in the bag of giblets[1] packed inside a grocery-store turkey.)

[1] **giblets:** the heart, liver, and gizzard of a turkey

1 What can you tell about the **main idea** of this selection from the first paragraph?

2 What are two **important details** in the second and third paragraphs about wild turkeys?

3 How does the turkey's eating habits and digestive system compare to that of other birds?

READING GUIDE

GUIDED QUESTIONS

Scientists have done experiments with turkeys to find out just how tough their gizzards are. In the 1600s an Italian professor named Giovanni Borelli pushed glass balls and lead cubes down the throats of several unfortunate turkeys. By the next day the glass balls were crumbled, and the metal cubes were **4** flattened. About a hundred years later another Italian, Lazzaro Spallanzani, discovered that a turkey gizzard could break up surgical knife blades. So, if a wild turkey swallows hard acorns or pecans with shells, no problem!

Turkeys eat together in family groups. A whole flock will march through a forest, its members **5** clucking to keep track of each other. The turkeys scratch through the fallen leaves with their feet to find nuts or pine seeds. At night they fly up into trees and **6** roost together.

Baby turkeys can walk almost as soon as they hatch. They follow their mothers around for protection from turkey-eaters such as bobcats, foxes, and owls. The babies eat lots of food, especially grasshoppers, and they grow fast. They can fly when they are only two weeks old.

Hundred of years ago, before any Europeans came to America, Native Americans hunted wild turkeys in the woods. They ate them and used their sparkly, multicolored feathers to decorate clothes, arrows, and blankets. They even made beads and spoons out of **7** turkey bones.

When the Pilgrims arrived in Massachusetts, they started eating the same wild turkeys the Indians were already eating. Naturally, several turkeys ended up in the first Thanksgiving dinner in 1621. That is how our **8** custom of having turkey on Thanksgiving got started.

4 How would you **summarize** the experiments that scientists have done with turkeys?

5 What causes turkeys to cluck as they march? What **effect** does the clucking have on the turkeys?

6 What can you **infer** about a turkey's desire for company?

7 **Retell** how Native Europeans used wild turkeys.

8 Explain how the Thanksgiving custom of eating turkey happened.

Go on to the next page ➡

READING GUIDE

That was nearly four hundred years ago. Most of us don't find wild turkeys on our dinner plates now. The turkeys we buy at the grocery store are extra-heavy ones that were raised on turkey farms. Those turkeys are not smart enough to survive in the woods. The only thing they ever eat is turkey feed made from ground corn and soybeans with vitamins and minerals **9** added.

But it's fun to imagine what would happen if a real, live wild turkey showed up at your house on **10** Thanksgiving. It could gobble up the salad greens, the fruits, the corn, some chestnuts or mushrooms from the stuffing, pecans from the pie. . . Hey do you ever serve grasshoppers?

Sample Extended Response Question

Explain what you would expect this selection to be about based on the title. Then give your opinion about whether or not you think the title fits with the **1** selection. Support your opinion with details or information from the article.

GUIDED QUESTIONS

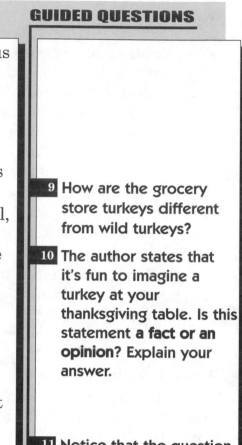

9 How are the grocery store turkeys different from wild turkeys?

10 The author states that it's fun to imagine a turkey at your thanksgiving table. Is this statement **a fact or an opinion?** Explain your answer.

11 Notice that the question asks you to decide whether or not the title makes sense for this selection.

 Measuring Up to the OH Learning Outcomes • Reading

Activity

Directions Answer the extended response question. Use the lines below.

_____

_____

_____

_____

_____

_____

_____

_____

_____

_____

_____

_____

_____

_____

Self Evaluation

Ask yourself
- Did I explain what the title means and what I expected the text to be about?
- Did I state whether or not I think the title fits the selection?
- Did I use support from the selection to back up my opinion?
- Is my answer clear and easy to read?

Your answer will be evaluated on a scale from 0-4. Aim to write a response that receives a 4. Teachers will use this rubric to evaluate your answer.

Extended-Response Rubric

4	• Provides extensive evidence of the kind of interpretation called for in the item or question • Is well organized, elaborate, and thorough • Demonstrates a complete understanding of the whole work as well as how the parts blend to form the whole • Is relevant, comprehensive, and detailed, demonstrating a thorough understanding of the reading selection • Addresses thoroughly the important elements of the question • Contains logical reasoning and communicates effectively and clearly *(A four-point response may go beyond the requirements of the item.)*
3	• Provides evidence that essential interpretation has been made • Is thoughtful and reasonably accurate • Indicates an understanding of the concept or item • Communicates adequately, and generally reaches reasonable conclusions • Contains some combination of the following flaws: 　◆ Minor flaws in reasoning or interpretation 　◆ Failure to address some aspect of the item or omission of some detail
2	• Is mostly accurate and relevant • Contains some combination of the following flaws: 　● Incomplete evidence of interpretation 　● Unsubstantiated statements made about the text 　● Incomplete understanding of the concept or item 　● Lack of comprehensiveness, faulty reasoning, unclear communication

 Measuring Up to the OH Learning Outcomes • Reading

1	• Provides little evidence of interpretation
	• Is unorganized and incomplete
	• Exhibits decoding rather than reading
	• Demonstrates a partial understanding of the item, but is sketchy and unclear
	• Indicates some effort beyond restating the item
	• Contains some combination of the following flaws:
	◆ Little understanding of the concept or item
	◆ Failure to address most aspects of the item
	◆ Inability to make coherent meaning from the text

0	• Shows no understanding of the item or the student fails to respond to the item

Question

Explain what you would expect this selection to be about based on the title. Then give your opinion about whether or not you think the title fits with the selection. Support your opinion with details or information from the article.

Sample Answer

    I would expect this selection to be about the what turkeys eat for thanksgiving because that is the title. I don't really think that this title goes with the article. The article is about wild turkeys and their big appetites. I learned in this article that turkeys eat not only ordinary bird food, but also small animals such as frogs and salamanders. The article also tells how turkeys digest their food with their powerful gizzards. Although the article does tell about the Pilgrims and how wild turkeys were eaten at the first Thanksgiving, it doesn't actually tell what turkeys, themselves, eat for thanksgiving. In fact, turkeys don't have thanksgiving.

Go on to the next page

Evaluation

This response would receive a 4. It answers all aspects of the question. It gives a clear opinion about why the student doesn't believe the title fits with the selection. Actual details from the text are given to summarize some of the main points that the article discusses. The overall response is clear and well written. The details are accurate and the question is thoroughly answered.

Directions   Exchange responses with a partner. Using the rubric, evaluate each other's response. Write your evaluation of your partner's response on the lines below.

_____

_____

_____

_____

_____

Skill Builder

Proofreading is important to make sure that your writing is as error free as possible. Make sure you proofread your extended response before you turn it in.

Correct errors in:

- spelling
- punctuation
- grammar
- capitalization

Directions Practice your proofreading skills. Proofread the passage below. It contains ten errors. Underline or circle each error and correct it.

I expected this article to be about turkeys and how they are raised. so that we can eat them on Thanksgiving. although that's not what the article focused on, I still think its a great title and it goes with the selection. At the end of the article, the author let us imagine a wild turkey joining our Thanksgiving feast and everything that the turkey would eat.

Even though everyone know that turkies don't celebrate thanksgiving, I still thought the title was amusing and it got me interested in reading the article The article talks about wild turkeys, what they eat, how they live in social groups, and how native Americans used them. The turkeys we eat for Thanksgiving are not wild turkeys, they are farm raised turkeys which eat turkey fead. Therefore, the article actually does mention what turkeys eat in order to be prepared for "hour" Thanksgiving.

Directions: Read the selection below and answer the questions that follow. You will complete five multiple choice questions, one short response question, and one extended response question.

Grandma Moses: Making the Most of Life
Pat McCarthy

The tiny gray-haired woman walked briskly up the sidewalk to her house in Eagle Bridge, New York. The door flew open. "Grandma," cried her daughter-in-law Dorothy, "if you had been here, you could have sold all your paintings! There was a man here looking for them, and he will be back in the morning to see them." Dorothy had told the man that Grandma had about ten paintings.

Grandma hardly slept that night. She got up early and found nine pictures. She cut one big painting in half and put it in two frames so there would be ten. "I did it so it wouldn't get Dorothy in the doghouse," she explained later.

Grandma's real name was Anna Mary Robertson Moses. She didn't become serious about painting until she was in her mid-seventies. She was almost eighty when she sold those first paintings in 1938. The man who bought them was Louis J. Caldor, an art collector.

He helped to get Grandma's pictures into a show of many artists' work at a New York City museum. Then, in 1940, an art gallery held a show of Grandma's pictures all by themselves. But Grandma didn't go to either show. She said she had already seen the paintings!

A month later, Grandma did go to New York. Gimbels' department store invited her to see a display of her pictures at its Thanksgiving festival. Here, people got to know Grandma Moses and her art. Grandma charmed everyone with her lively personality. Her paintings of happy times in the country made people feel good about the world.

As years passed, people became even more interested in Grandma and her work. In 1955, the famous news reporter Edward R. Murrow invited her to be on his TV show, *See It Now*.

On the program, people watched Grandma paint a picture at her house. She sat at her old tip-up table and painted on Masonite, a thin hard board. Grandma started with the sky, then painted the hills, trees, buildings, and people. "I like to paint old-timey things," she said. "I like pretty things the best."

Her work is called primitive[1] art, a style of art that is simple and clear. Like Grandma, many primitive artists have not had formal training. But Grandma used her memory, and studied the color of the world outside. This helped her add true-to-life details to her paintings. They show activities such as catching the Thanksgiving turkey, ice-skating, and bringing in the maple sap.

Grandma lived to be 101 and was always active. In the last year of her life, she painted twenty-five pictures.

In a book she wrote about herself, Grandma said, "I look back on my life like a good day's work: it was done and I feel satisfied with it. I was happy and contented. . .and made the best out of what life offered." By making the best of her life, Grandma made people happy with her paintings.

---

[1]**primitive** very simple and basic; unschooled

Go On

1. What can you infer about why Grandma barely slept the night before the man came to buy her paintings?

  ○ **A.** she was nervous he would steal them

  ○ **B.** she was excited to sell them

  ○ **C.** she didn't feel well because she was old

2. Which is **not** a reason that Grandma's art was called *primitive* art?

  ○ **A.** it was simple and clear

  ○ **B.** Grandma never had formal training

  ○ **C.** Grandma painted scenes of cavemen

3. Which of the following statements from the selection is more an opinion than a fact?

  ○ **A.** Grandma didn't go to either show.

  ○ **B.** In the last year of her life, she painted twenty-five pictures.

  ○ **C.** Grandma made people happy with her paintings.

4. What effect did Grandma's paintings of happy times in the country have on people?

  ○ **A.** they made people feel good about the world

  ○ **B.** they made people want to take vacations in the country

  ○ **C.** they made people angry about problems in the city

5. What statement best summarizes the main idea of this selection?

    A. Grandma Moses was an old artist.

    B. Grandma Moses painted simple things that people enjoyed looking at.

    C. Grandma was not a serious painter for most of her life.

6. Why did Grandma cut one painting in half? Why did she feel that she needed to do this?

_____

_____

_____

_____

7. Retell the story of how Grandma sold her first paintings and how she began to become well-known as an artist.

_____

_____

_____

_____

_____

_____

_____

_____

Choose Resources to Make Decisions and Solve Problems

1. Think about your favorite sport or hobby. Now imagine that you are going to write a short report about it. At the library, you will decide which resources you will use. Fill in the chart below with specific names or titles of resources that you can use for this report. Try to find a resource to write in each column of the chart.

Books	Magazine or Newspaper Articles	Encyclopedias or Other Reference Materials	Internet Sites

Choose Resources to Make Decisions and Solve Problems (cont'd)

2. Do you like to solve problems? In this activity, you will have the opportunity to find nonfiction resources to help you solve problems. For each problem listed in the chart below, find at least one nonfiction resource that offers information, ideas, or solutions. Then list some ideas or solutions.

Problem	Nonfiction Resources	Ideas or Solutions
Where to go for our end-of-the-year class trip		
Recycling in our neighborhood		
Kids need after-school activity ideas.		
You got a gerbil for your birthday and you've never taken care of a pet before.		

Speaking/Listening Activity

Look through a newspaper or magazine in your house. Find a nonfiction article that interests you. Read the article and summarize it in your head. Then tell some family members what it was about and have a discussion about it. If someone has a question, see if you can answer it based on what you read. If no one knows the answer to the question, come up with a list of resources you could turn to in order to find an answer.

Reading Activity

People like to read about things that interest them. Choose someone in your family and think of an interest that he or she has. For instance, you may have a parent who is interested in cooking, fishing, knitting, or antique collecting. You may have a brother or sister who is interested in painting, juggling, stamp collecting, or baseball. Then go on an information hunt. Find books, magazines, brochures, or even Internet sites about this topic. Collect as many resources as you can and present them as a gift to your family member. If the materials need to be returned to the library, remind the person that the gift is a temporary loan.

Notes

Notes

Copying is Illegal.